MACMILLAN McGRAW-HILL
Science

Lucy H. Daniel

Jay Hackett

Richard H. Moyer

JoAnne Vasquez

About the Cover

Lambs are baby sheep. The father sheep is called
a ram and the mother sheep is called a ewe. Sheep
are mammals with thick, woolly fur and hoofed
feet. There are many types of wild sheep which
are closely related to wild goats. Domestic or tame
sheep are farmed for their meat, milk, and wool.
Sheep are herbivores (plant-eaters) and they mostly
graze on grass, leaves, twigs, and young plants.

Inquiry Skill Compare How are baby lambs
the same as their mothers and fathers? How are
they differrent?

Program Authors

Dr. Lucy H. Daniel
Teacher, Consultant
Rutherford County Schools, North Carolina

Dr. Jay Hackett
Professor Emeritus of Earth Sciences
University of Northern Colorado

Dr. Richard H. Moyer
Professor of Science Education
University of Michigan-Dearborn

Dr. JoAnne Vasquez
Elementary Science Education Consultant
Mesa Public Schools, Arizona
NSTA Past President

Contributing Authors

Lucille Villegas Barrera, M.Ed.
Elementary Science Supervisor
Houston Independent School District
Houston, Texas

Becky Manfredini and Jenny Resnick
Kids at Heart
Calabasas, California

Mulueheta Teferi, M.A.
St. Louis Public Schools
St. Louis, Missouri

Bank Street Contributing Authors

Jessica Bacal, M.A.
Curriculum Developer
Bank Street College of Education
New York, New York

Kathleen Hayes, M.L.S, M.A.
Curriculum and Staff Developer
External Affairs
Bank Street College of Education
New York, New York

Laura Sedlock, M.A.
Head Teacher, Beginnings Nursery School
New York, New York

The **McGraw·Hill** *Companies*

**Macmillan
McGraw-Hill**

Published by Macmillan/McGraw-Hill, of McGraw-Hill Education, a division of The McGraw-Hill Companies, Inc.,
Two Penn Plaza, New York, New York 10121.

Teacher Reviewers

Michelle Dunning
Birmingham, Alabama

Donna Bullock
Chandler, Arizona

Debra Allen
Davie, Florida

Lora Meade
Plantation, Florida

Roxanne Laird
Miami, Florida

Karen Gaudy
Satellite Beach, Florida

Stephanie Sirianni
Margate, Florida

Heidi Stephens
South Daytona, Florida

Rosanne Phillips
Miami, Florida

Brenda Crow
Miami, Florida

Kari Pingel
Pella, Iowa

Christie Jones
Springfield, Illinois

Diane Songer
Wabash, Indiana

Lee Arwood
Wabash, Indiana

Margarite Hart
Indianapolis, Indiana

Charlotte Bennett
Newburgh, Indiana

Donna Halverson
Evansville, Indiana

Stephanie Tanke
Crown Point, Indiana

Mindey LeMoine
Marquette, Michigan

Billie Bell
Grand View, Missouri

Charlotte Sharp
Greenville, North Carolina

Pat Shane
Chapel Hill, North Carolina

Karen Daniel
Chapel Hill, North Carolina

Linda Dow
Concord, North Carolina

Beth Lewis
Wilmington, North Carolina

Cindy Hatchell
Wilmington, North Carolina

Cindy Kahler
Carrborro, North Carolina

Diane Leusky
Chapel Hill, North Carolina

Heather Sutton
Wilmington, North Carolina

Crystal Stephens
Valdese, North Carolina

Meg Millard
Chapel Hill, North Carolina

Patricia Underwood
Randleman, North Carolina

E. Joy Mermin
Chapel Hill, North Carolina

Yolanda Evans
Wilmington, North Carolina

Tim Gilbride
Pennsauken, New Jersey

Helene Reifowitz
Nesconsit, New York

Tina Craig
Tulsa, Oklahoma

Deborah Harwell
Lawton, Oklahoma

Kathleen Conn
West Chester, Pennsylvania

Heath Renninger Zerbe
Tremont, Pennsylvania

Patricia Armillei
Holland, Pennsylvania

Sue Workman
Cedar City, Utah

Peg Jensen
Hartford, Wisconsin

About the Cover

Lambs are baby sheep. Sheep are mammals with thick, woolly fur and hoofed feet. The father sheep is called a ram and the mother sheep is called a ewe. A ewe can have up to three babies a year. A lamb can walk minutes after it is born. It drinks milk from its mother for about four months and then it eats grass, leaves, young plants, and grain. Sheep are herbivores or plant-eaters. The usual life span of sheep ranges from about six to eleven years old, but sometimes they can live to be as old as twenty.

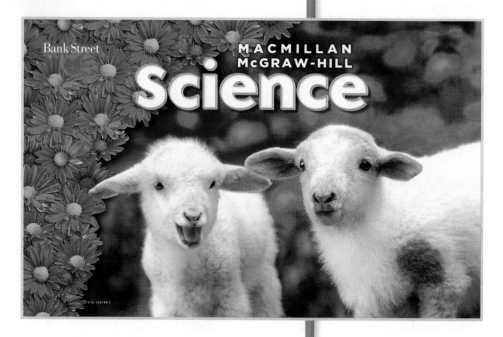

Sheep can be milked just like cows and their milk is used to make things such as cheese and yogurt. Their fleece, or fur, can be used to produce wool for many things like hats, sweaters, and coats. The fat from sheep can be used to make items such as candles and soap.

 Visit **www.macmillanmh.com** to learn more about lambs and sheep.

Music/Movement Activity

Sing the song *Mary Had a Little Lamb* to children. Then sing it again, inviting children to join you. Encourage partners to act out the song as they sing. Then invite children to "baa" like sheep.

Inquiry Skill Observe Display the cover and ask children to tell about what they see. (Accept all answers.)

UNIT A

Be a Scientist

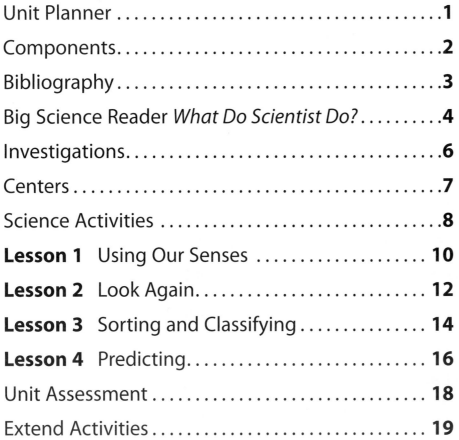

Life Science

UNIT B

Plants

UNIT C

Animals

Earth Science

UNIT E

Sky and Weather

UNIT F

Matter and Motion

FOR YOUR REFERENCE

Dear Educators,

Pre-K is a very special time for children. As they enter Pre-K, children bring with them a natural curiosity about the world around them. The Macmillan/McGraw-Hill Pre-Kindergarten Science Program, a collaboration between Macmillan/McGraw-Hill and Bank Street College of Education, is designed to build on their curiosity and help children engage in direct, hands-on investigations as they explore the world around them.

We believe that children's learning should proceed naturally from their daily lives. Children learn best when they are allowed and encouraged to interact with animals, plants, objects, ideas, peers, and teachers to build their own understanding of the world around them. We believe that the best learning environments for young children are those that provide a rich variety of appropriate materials and experiences with teacher support to strengthen their fast growing expressive and receptive language skills.

This science program promotes children's active participation in center based, small, and whole group activities. The lessons and materials are designed to help you integrate science throughout your day. The program is designed to encourage children to communicate their ideas, make discoveries on their own, and share those discoveries with others. It will also help them begin to acquire the all-important science inquiry skills that they will use throughout their lives as they observe, measure, compare, classify, make models, communicate, infer, put things in order, predict, investigate, and draw conclusions. We think you will find Macmillan/McGraw-Hill Science a great help as you guide and support children's explorations in science.

Augusta Souza Kappner, President
Bank Street College of Education

Bank Street

Focus on Pre-Kindergarten

Program Philosophy

Macmillan/McGraw-Hill Science engages the curiosity that young children naturally bring with them to school. This dynamic program uses the 5 E Model: Engage, Explore, Explain, Extend, and Evaluate, to deliver a comprehensive science curriculum.

Macmillan/McGraw-Hill Science builds on children's prior experiences, backgrounds, and early theories. It draws on children's curiosity and encourages children to pursue their own questions and develop their own ideas. The activities and materials engage children in in-depth exploration of topics over time in a carefully prepared environment.

The lessons and activities encourage children to reflect on, represent, and document their experiences as the children share and discuss their ideas with others. It allows the teacher to embed the science curriculum in children's daily work and play, and to integrate science with other domains. Macmillan/McGraw-Hill Science provides access to science experiences for all children.

(adapted from *Worms, Shadows, and Whirlpools: Science in the Early Childhood Classroom*, p. 14)

Pre-Kindergarten Science Components

Flipbook

An interactive flipbook featuring rich photographs to convey science content.

Teacher's Edition

Organized into six units that provide a variety of investigations and activities to help young children explore the world around them.

Big Science Readers

Two volumes of photographic non-fiction stories and colorfully illustrated poems that provide support for science instruction.

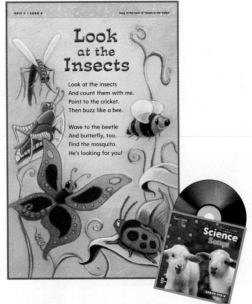

Science Materials Kit

Provides essential materials to be used with activities throughout this program.

Photo Sorting Cards

Sixty pairs of cards that support visual literacy, and can be used with math, reading, and science activities.

Science Songs Audio CD
Science Songs Posters

Twelve songs and instrumental tracks accompanied by posters that help support science instruction.

Why Science in Pre-K?

With the increasing emphasis on emergent literacy skill instruction in the youngest grades, why should a Pre-K teacher make time for science?

- Perhaps most importantly, because young children are curious. They are trying to make sense of what happens in the world around them. They do this by building theories of their own to explain what they see.

- Preschool teachers can use this natural ability and desire to make sense of the world around them by helping children use science inquiry skills. Even preschool children can begin to: *observe, compare, measure, classify, communicate, infer, make a model, predict, investigate, and draw a conclusion.*

Building Theories, A Step at a Time

A group of 4-year-olds were walking near a pond. They were collecting leaves, twigs, and stones to bring back to the classroom science center. Lisa, one of the 4-year-olds, stopped to look at a Norway spruce. She ran her fingers through the pine needles and then moved closer to the tree and ran her fingers over the bark. She turned to Nina, the assistant teacher, and asked her if she wanted to feel the "prickles."

Nina asked Lisa, "Is this pine tree like any of the other trees around here?" She thought Lisa might say that some trees look like the pine tree, but that others, like the oak and maple trees look different. Instead, Lisa said,

"Well, all the trees are green. And that's because the pond water splashes up and colors the trees green."

Nina's open-ended question allowed Lisa to share her theories about trees. Her answer was inaccurate, but it represents some critical thinking on her part. Lisa's response shows that she is exploring patterns and relationships within the environment. She has also made an imaginative association with the green color of the pond surface. (In fact, the water looks green because it is reflecting the color of the trees.) Lisa was trying to put together what she knew in order to understand something else. She was thinking like a scientist.

(adapted from Explorations with *Young Children: A Curriculum Guide from the Bank Street College of Education*, pages 194-195)

Lisa's teacher will use the information she learned by listening to Lisa explain her theory, and help her refine her thinking. She might plan a trip to the pond on a cloudy day and help Lisa think about the color of the pond water. Lisa is probably not yet able to understand how water reflects the color of the trees, but she could observe that the pond water seems to change color from day to day. Her theory for why that is so may still be "incorrect" but that is not what is significant. What is important is that Lisa is really thinking. Her teacher encourages that thinking process and applauds the steps she takes towards a deeper understanding, based on her own observations and inquiry.

Science Content

What the Research Says...

The National Science Education Standards emphasize that from the earliest grades, children must:

- Develop the ability to ask their own questions.

- Answer them by seeking information from reliable sources and from their own observations and investigations.

(National Science Education Standards, p. 121)

Macmillan/McGraw-Hill Science is designed to help you create an inquiry-based science program.

 Inquiry into authentic questions generated from student experiences is the central strategy for teaching science.

(National Science Education Standards, p. 31)

In **Macmillan/McGraw-Hill Science:**

- Each unit begins by asking children to share what they know. Young children learn best when they link what is familiar to them with new experiences, ideas and concepts.

- The images and questions found in the Pre-K Flipbook are designed to encourage broad child participation in science discussions.

 At all stages of inquiry, teachers guide, focus, challenge, and encourage student learning.

(National Science Education Standards, p. 33)

In **Macmillan/McGraw-Hill Science:**

- Each unit includes a variety of small-group, hands-on activities that will help you observe, support, and extend the children's learning.

- Informal assessment strategies are offered throughout the unit to help you focus your observations. This will enable you to more effectively plan curriculum for the entire group and respond to the needs of individual children.

Effective science teaching depends on the availability and organization of materials, equipment, media, and technology. **77**

(National Science Education Standards, p. 44)

In **Macmillan/McGraw-Hill Science:**

■ The topics in this science program can be explored over the course of several weeks or months. The flexibility of the program components and activity suggestions will enable you to incorporate science instruction throughout your day.

■ Multiple online resources and bibliographies in the Teacher's Edition will enrich your planning and lesson implementation.

An important stage of inquiry and of student science learning is the oral discourse that focuses the attention of students on how they know what they know and how their knowledge connects to larger ideas, other domains, and the world beyond the classroom. **77**

(National Science Education Standards, p. 36)

In **Macmillan/McGraw-Hill Science:**

■ Each lesson helps you ask questions that will promote critical thinking skills and create lively whole-class, small-group, and one-on-one discussions.

■ Each unit contains activity and center suggestions that help you integrate what you are doing in science throughout your day.

■ The Big Science Readers, Songs Posters, and Photo Sorting Cards that accompany this program provide additional science content to support your literacy instruction.

Teachers must have theoretical and practical knowledge and abilities about science, learning, and science teaching. **77**

(National Science Education Standards, p. 28)

In **Macmillan/McGraw-Hill Science:**

■ Each lesson provides "Science Facts" that give you additional information about the content of the lesson.

■ Activity suggestions were conceived and written by experienced teachers who recognize and take into account the realities of early childhood classroom life.

■ There is a glossary of scientific terms written specifically for the early childhood teacher to support his/her science background.

Teachers who are enthusiastic, interested, and who speak of the power and beauty of scientific understanding instill in their students some of those same attitudes. **77**

(National Science Education Standards, p. 37)

In **Macmillan/McGraw-Hill Science:**

■ The materials and activities are designed to help teachers and children observe and marvel at the beauty of the world around them.

■ Lessons and materials support children's talk with interested adults and peers about what they observe and experience.

Talking Science

What the Research Says...

 An important stage of inquiry and of science learning is the oral discourse that focuses the attention of children on how they know what they know and how their knowledge connects to larger ideas, other domains, and the world beyond the classroom.

(adapted, National Science Education Standards, p. 36)

Beginning Your Science Work

Support children's natural curiosity by creating meaningful, hands-on science experiences. You can also help them learn how to investigate their own questions.

In order to meet such goals, you must find time to:

- Listen to what they say.
- Encourage them to ask questions.
- Respond to their questions, not with answers, but with a question instead.

Responding with a question helps children think deeper about a topic, share more of what they know, and may even help them formulate tentative answers to their own questions.

Developing Questioning Strategies

When we ask children questions, it is often because we want to find out if they know something.

- You might begin your science work by asking: **What do you think scientists do?**

- If a child responds by saying: "They look at things," you might be tempted to say: "That's right," and record their response on a chart. Then move on to another child.

- Here is an alternative way to respond: **What kind of things do they look at?** This question gives children an opportunity to share more of their thinking. You might find out that they know scientists look at stars or dinosaur bones. Their response to this question gives you information about what they know, and what they might be curious to know more about.

- You could continue to ask questions to probe further: **Why do you think they look at stars or dinosaur bones?**

Sometimes you will have to answer children's questions with answers. They may insist on an answer from you, or you may not have time to engage in this kind of in-depth discussion at that moment. Remember you can also respond by saying:

- **That is a good question. We do not have time to talk about it now, but I will write it down so we can discuss it later.**

- **I am not sure, what do you think?**

- **I do not know. How could we find out?**

Addressing Misconceptions

As teachers, we are anxious to cover all the standards, teach all the necessary vocabulary, and make sure children know certain "science facts." However, we know that children's behavior and thinking develop over time. They are continually revising their understanding of the world, and no matter what we tell them, they might not be able to understand it yet. We must be careful not to correct children's misconceptions too soon.

Doing What Scientists Do

One Pre-kindergarten teacher, who had guinea pigs in her classroom, was introducing a rabbit to the group. She asked the children: "What do you know about rabbits?" One child said that guinea pigs grew up to be rabbits.

The teacher responded by asking: "Why do you think that?" The child said that as guinea pigs grew, their ears would become longer and they would turn into rabbits.

Why this response? The child was using what she knew to try and figure something out.

- She knew her own body parts were getting bigger over time.

- She knew that rabbit ears were long and that rabbits had fur and four legs.

- She also knew guinea pigs had fur and four legs.

It is not correct, but she was putting together the information she had gathered about the way things work in the world and was trying to make sense of it. She was doing what a scientist would do.

Rather than just tell the child that was incorrect, the teacher asked: "Since we have both guinea pigs and a rabbit in our classroom, how could we find out if guinea pigs turn into rabbits?"

- Some children said they should watch the guinea pigs to see what happened.

- Another child shared that she had guinea pigs at home and one got really old and died, but it never turned into a rabbit.

- Now the children were able to weigh this new evidence and draw their own conclusions.

In this meeting, the children talked and listened to one another. The teacher facilitated this discussion by asking questions that helped children share their thinking. She did not just tell children the answers. As a result, they discovered that they could work together to draw conclusions and develop plans to investigate a question that was important to them.

Talking seriously about science and "doing" science together can be an exciting, rewarding experience for you and your class. This type of science teaching helps children craft their own questions, develop hypotheses, and work together to investigate possible answers to their questions.

For more information, read:

Doing What Scientist's Do: Children Learn to Investigate Their World, by Ellen Doris (Heinemann, 1991)

Your Science Center

Early Materials

Do not be afraid to place only a few carefully chosen materials in the Science Center, especially at the beginning of the year. Too many materials can overwhelm children and discourage focused observation.

- Begin by placing some healthy potted plants in the center. Show children how to check the dirt before adding water. When you begin your formal study of plants in Unit B, children will have had some practice caring for and informally observing the plants in the center.

- Add some science observation sheets in a folder or basket and show children where to write their names and add the date stamp so you can file the observational drawings in their portfolios. A small basket of colored pencils and/or crayons and some black pencils will invite drawing.

- A small collection of books that extend the work you are doing in each unit will invite browsing.

- As you begin Unit B, you will want to add some of the class projects (germinating seeds, seedlings) to the center for safe storage where children can observe change over time.

Sand/Water Table

If you have a Sand/Water Table, you may want to begin the year with sand in the table. The clean-up is easier and requires less teacher supervision than water.

- Be sure to include a small hand brush and dustpan near the Sand Table so children can clean up any sand that falls to the floor.

- If some of your children went to the beach in the summer, add some small stones and shovels. The memories of family beach activities that such materials evoke can be comforting for children who may be feeling some separation anxiety.

- As the year progresses, you will add other materials. For now, give children time to explore the sand, learn the clean-up routines, and enjoy "messing about" in a material that will later teach them much about volume and weight, and be used to create models of landforms.

Adding Class Pets

Once children in your room are comfortable and secure in their new classroom environment, you may want to add animals to your Science Center. They can be very important components of your year-long science work.

- By carefully introducing pets to the class and teaching children how to care for and treat them gently, you will foster lifelong skills that every child needs.

- If you choose pet(s) that have short growth cycles, children may be able to observe the complete life cycle of one or more species.

- The investment in a fish tank, filter, and cover will last many years and create an environment for cold-water fish, water snails, and plants.

- Before adding any furry pets, you will need to make sure no child has an allergy to the pet you are considering.

Be prepared to help children answer many of their own questions about the new pets.

- Collect a variety of nonfiction books that discuss the animal(s) you have added. Do not worry if some of them are written for older children. Your children will learn a great deal as they pore over the illustrations in the books.

- In Unit C, you will find that many of the suggested activities and investigations can be modified so that children can use the animal(s) in the Science Center to learn more about animal motion, coverings, adaptations, etc.

By the end of the year, children will know a great deal about the animals that you have included in the Science Center, and will have used the science inquiry skills needed to learn more about many other kinds of animals and plants.

In subsequent units, you will want to add materials to support the study of the earth and physical sciences, but keep the plants and animals in the center all year. You will be able to collect and analyze the drawings and observations children do of these livings things over the course of the year.

For more information on setting up and using centers, read:

Classroom Routines That Really Work for Pre-K and K,
by Kathleen Hayes and Renee Creange
(Scholastic, 2001)

Animals in the Classroom: Selection, Care, and Observation,
by David C. Kramer
(Addison-Wesley Longman, 1989)

The Developmental Profile of a Four-Year-Old

What the Research Says...

Social/Emotional

 Social interaction with peers and adults is essential for children to learn cooperation.

(The guidelines for Appropriate Curriculum Content and Assessment in Programs Serving Children Ages 3 through 8, NAEYC, 1990)

Preschool is a time when children learn how to share materials, their ideas, and their feelings. They need continued teacher support to learn the essential social skills needed to get along with others.

Macmillan/McGraw-Hill Science provides materials and activity suggestions that will enable you to support children's social and emotional development as they work together in centers.

■ Because most of the program materials and activities are designed to be included in your center time this program enables you to work with the children as they learn to cooperate with one another by sharing what they are thinking and discovering.

■ During center time you can support and extend children's thinking as they work together in the Science Center, the Block Area, at the Art Table, in the Math Center, or when children are looking at nonfiction books in the Library Center.

Physical

 Physical development is an integral part of children's well-being. A principle focus is on children's ability to move in ways that demonstrate control, balance and coordination. Fine motor skills are equally important in laying the groundwork for artistic expression, handwriting, and self-care skills.

(Jablon et al., 1994)

Children in Pre-K are gaining a sense of control of their bodies and a sense of themselves as competent learners.

Macmillan/McGraw-Hill Science provides opportunities for children to develop their physical abilities.

■ The materials in the Science Center give children the opportunity to actively engage with materials, developing eye hand coordination as they work with a balance scale, carefully tend plants and animals, observe and record data using pictures and words.

■ Going out into the field to study plants and animals will give children the opportunity to work outdoors.

■ Using the science songs will give children the opportunity to move, act out, and clap along as they sing the songs.

Cognitive

Even from the earliest grade levels, students should learn what constitutes evidence and judge the merits or strength of the data and information that will be used to make explanations.

(National Science Education Standards, p. 122)

Preschool children are capable of observing, describing and sharing their ideas with others. When teachers ask children to explain what they are doing or observing, they learn how to communicate their observations and discuss how/why they did something. These early experiences of direct, hands-on activities will lay a foundation for children's continued discovery and understanding of the world around them.

Macmillan/McGraw-Hill Science offers experiences that will help children refine and deepen their ability to think about what they see and do.

- The Circle Time Activities and small group science activities provide opportunities for children to explore and investigate, and then discuss what happened with both adults and their peers.

- Program materials help children improve their visual discrimination skills, and enhance their visual literacy skills as they work with Photo Sorting Cards, Flipbook pages, and Song Posters.

Language

Scientific literacy means that a person has the ability to describe, explain, and predict natural phenomena…it also implies the capacity to pose and evaluate arguments based on evidence and to apply conclusions from such arguments appropriately.

(National Science Education Standards, p. 22)

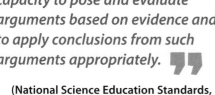

Preschool children need many opportunities to communicate their ideas to peers and adults. They also need teacher support to learn words that will accurately describe what they see or experience, and to use evidence to justify their tentative conclusions.

Macmillan/McGraw-Hill Science provides a variety of ways to help children learn how to talk together.

- Each page in the Flipbook is designed to provide opportunities for children to talk about what they see.

- Many activities are designed for small groups with teacher support so children can learn to interact more fully with peers and adults.

- Easy-to-memorize song texts teach new vocabulary and provide opportunities for all children to participate.

- The Big Science Readers provide an introduction to hearing non-fiction and poetry read aloud. The close relationship between text and illustrations will help children learn new vocabulary related to specific science content.

- The images on the Photo Sorting Cards provide a strong word-image correlation. The multiple sets of cards allow children to play games like Concentration and Go-fish. These games will give children multiple experiences with the images. Children will be able to accurately name a variety of objects, animals, and plants.

The Pre-Kindergarten Classroom

Even the youngest students can and should participate in discussions and decisions about using time and space for work. The more independently students can access what they need, the more they can take responsibility for their own work.

(National Science Education Standards, p. 45)

Macmillan/McGraw-Hill Science provides ideas and suggestions for creating a well-organized and well-equipped classroom that invites scientific exploration and discovery.

Art Center

Children can explore properties of matter as they:

- Cut, tear, fold, bend, and arrange paper or cloth when they make collages.
- Combine a variety of materials into sculptures.
- Explore color mixing as they paint and draw with pastels or chalk.
- Shape clay, play dough, and other pliable materials.

Dramatic Play Center

The dramatic play area fosters cooperative play and expressive and receptive language skills as children:

- Represent what they saw or did on a trip.
- Create their own play script that incorporates information learned in the science curriculum, e.g., what animals do in the winter.

Water/Sand Table

Children can explore science as they:

- Pour and measure sand or water.
- Investigate how water flows by using tubes and funnels.
- Create dioramas of animal habitats.
- Explore properties of matter as they investigate what sinks and what floats, and draw tentative conclusions from that investigation.
- Experience the pleasure of working with sensorial materials.

Block Center

When building in the block area, children discover:

- Principles of balance, design, and symmetry.
- How to plan and build structures that please their eye.
- How to work cooperatively with others to share the limited resources of the block area.
- Principles of physics as blocks tumble, cars roll, and things slide over and around ramps.

Unit Planner

Be a Scientist

Lesson	Objective	Resources
1 Using Our Five Senses pp. 10–11	Children will learn about the five senses.	Flipbook, p. 1
2 Look Again pp. 12–13	Children will learn to compare and observe closely.	Flipbook, p. 2
3 Sorting and Classifying pp. 14–15	Children will learn to sort and classify objects.	Flipbook, p. 3
4 Predicting pp. 16–17	Children will learn to predict events.	Flipbook, p. 4

Flipbook

Use pages 1–4 to help children learn about the five senses, how to look carefully at their world, how to sort and classify, and for opportunities to predict what might happen next.

Big Science Reader

For Unit A, the story *What Do Scientists Do?* exposes children to the different ways scientists explore our world. It gives children the opportunity to practice observing, using tools, and comparing similarities and differences.

Science Songs (CD and Posters)

You can use the songs *Use Your Senses* (tracks 1–2) and *You Can Sort* (tracks 3–4) for an exciting way to learn about the five senses and sorting. Children can use the posters to help them sing along as they discover the world around them.

Materials

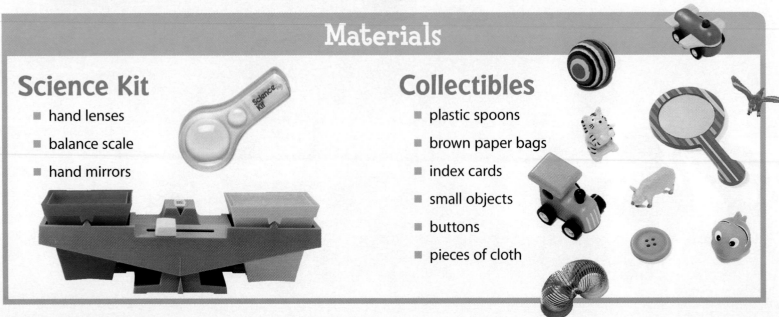

Science Kit

- hand lenses
- balance scale
- hand mirrors

Collectibles

- plastic spoons
- brown paper bags
- index cards
- small objects
- buttons
- pieces of cloth

Unit Bibliography

Do You Want To Be My Friend?, by Eric Carle
(Putnam, 1988)

Use this and other predictable books to help children predict what might happen next.

Farm Alphabet Book, by Jane Miller
(Scholastic, 1981)

Use this book for more information about life on a farm. You can use this book to expose the children to all the letters in the alphabet.

Guinea Pig ABC, by Kate Duke
(Puffin/Penguin Putnam, 1986)

Explore the letters of the alphabet and notice how the guinea pigs in this book are alike and different.

My Five Senses, by Margaret Miller
(Simon and Schuster, 1994)

You can use the format of this book to make a class book about senses using photographs or pictures of objects from your own classroom.

My Spring Robin, by Anne Rockwell
(Simon & Schuster, 1996)

Share this book about a young child who looks carefully and discovers many interesting plants and animals in her own backyard. Then take a trip in your schoolyard to see what your students can find.

The Button Box, by Margarette S. Reid
(Dutton 1990)

Use this book for more practice with sorting and classifying buttons.

The Pumpkin Book, by Gail Gibbons
(Holiday House, 1999)

Learn more about pumpkins by reading this book about the growth and use of pumpkins.

School-to-Home

Be sure to send home the Home Letter on p. R1 with an activity that your students can do with their families.

Start the Year UNIT A • Be a Scientist

Dear Parents,

This year, we will be learning a lot about science, and helping your children learn how to think and act as scientists do. Scientists use what we call "inquiry skills" to do their work. They observe, compare, measure, classify (organize objects by like characteristics), communicate their questions and observations, put things in order (for example, from shortest to longest), make models, predict, investigate and draw conclusions.

When you take a walk in the park or go grocery shopping with your child, you can help them begin to use these inquiry skills. Ask questions such as, *What do you see? Which one is the biggest? How do you know that?* As you talk together, you will be helping your child learn how to think and act as scientists do.

Thanks for your support as we begin our work together this year.

Bank Street

For more information on these or other books, visit **www.bankstreetbooks.com** or your local library.

Big Science Reader

Volume 1

Before Reading

- Ask children what they think scientists do. (Accept all answers.)
- Show children the table of contents and model looking for the page number of the non-fiction selection, *What Do Scientists Do?*

During Reading

- After reading the first two pages, discuss the different sizes, wing shapes, color, patterns and anything else children notice. Point out that we use our eyes to notice things in our world.
- Using pp. 2–3, encourage children to notice the attributes of the cats that are the same and those that are different. List on chart paper the children's responses. (Possible Responses: fur, whiskers, four legs, a tail, color, size, position)

What Do Scientists Do?

Scientists learn by looking carefully at things.

Look carefully at these butterflies. What do you see?

1

Scientists observe how things are the same and different.

2

How are these cats the same? How are they different?

3

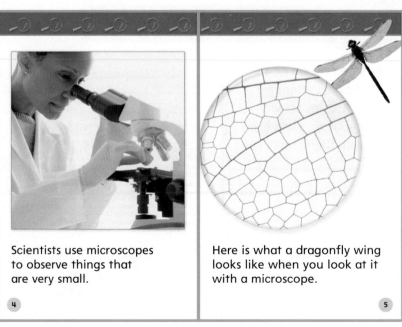

Scientists use microscopes to observe things that are very small.

4

Here is what a dragonfly wing looks like when you look at it with a microscope.

5

Scientists use telescopes to observe things that are far away.

6

Here is what the Moon looks like when you look at it through a telescope.

7

You can look carefully just as scientists do.

8

After Reading

- Ask children to discuss things they can do that scientists do.

- Model using a hand lens to examine a small object from the Science Center and describe what you see. Explain that you will place hand lenses in the Science Center so they can use them and describe what they see.

Teacher Tip

To save time, instead of passing a hand lens around, reassure children that everyone will get a turn to use them in the Science Center.

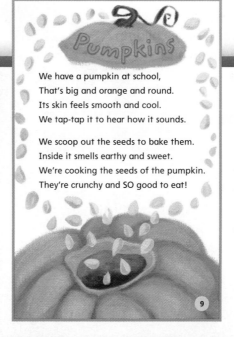

Pumpkins

We have a pumpkin at school,
That's big and orange and round.
Its skin feels smooth and cool.
We tap-tap it to hear how it sounds.

We scoop out the seeds to bake them.
Inside it smells earthy and sweet.
We're cooking the seeds of the pumpkin.
They're crunchy and SO good to eat!

9

Read the poem *Pumpkins,* on page 9 in the Big Science Reader, vol. 1, inviting children to join in on parts they remember. Discuss the different body parts and senses we use. Reread this poem throughout the unit. See page 31 in the Big Science Reader for more reading strategies.

Be a Scientist

 30 MINUTES   **WHOLE CLASS** **Investigation**

Exploring Pumpkins

Objective: Learn about pumpkins using the senses.

Science Inquiry Skills: observe, compare, predict

Materials
- small pumpkin
- sharp knife
- spoons

1 **Observe** Place a pumpkin in the center of the meeting area. Allow children to touch the pumpkin on the outside. Ask children to describe how the pumpkin looks and feels. Record responses on chart paper. Explain that we use our hands to touch things in our world.

2 During Center Time, have small groups of children work with you to pull out the strings and seeds. Encourage them to smell the inside of the pumpkin and point out that we use our nose to smell things.

3 **Compare** After Center Time, ask the whole group to describe how the pumpkin felt on the inside compared to how it felt on the outside. Record responses.

4 Cut the pumpkin into pieces, place one piece in a plastic bag, and leave in the Science Center for a week and put the other pieces in a refrigerator.

5 **Predict** Ask children what they think might happen to the pieces of pumpkin. Then after a week, have children observe the pieces of pumpkin and confirm their predictions.

centers

Art

Fingerprints

Materials
- ink pads
- drawing paper

Objective: Notice details in different fingerprints.

Science Inquiry Skills: observe, compare, communicate

- Have children use the ink pad to make their thumbprint on a sheet of paper.
- Working with a partner, help children notice the differences between their fingerprints.
- Explain that we all have unique fingerprints.

Math

Balancing Act

Materials
- pumpkin
- balance scale
- small objects

Objective: Compare weights of objects.

Science Inquiry Skills: compare, observe, measure

- Place a small pumpkin on one side of a balance scale and objects on the other side so that it is balanced.
- Explain that when the scale is balanced, the pumpkin and the group of objects on the other side weigh the same.
- Remove and add objects and ask which weighs more each time.
- Have children use other objects to compare weights with the pumpkin.

Cooking

Pumpkin Seeds

Materials
- pumpkin seeds
- oil
- cookie sheet
- salt

Objective: Learn that we can eat some seeds.

Science Inquiry Skills: observe

- Wash and dry the pumpkin seeds.
- Have children help arrange seeds over a thin layer of oil on a cookie sheet.
- Sprinkle with salt.
- Place in a 350 degree oven until toasted.

Games

Match It Up!

Materials
- Photo Sorting Cards #1–10

Objective: Learn how to observe closely and match Photo Sorting Cards.

Science Inquiry Skills: compare, observe, classify

- Help children arrange the Photo Sorting Cards face down in rows.
- A player turns over two cards. If they make a match, the player keeps them. If not, they are turned face down and the next player takes a turn.
- Play continues until all matches have been found.

caterpillar · caterpillar · butterfly · butterfly

Science Activities

Circle Time

WHOLE CLASS

Materials
• pink eraser
• brown bag

Guess What!

Objective: Use the senses to identify objects.

Science Inquiry Skills: infer, draw a conclusion, observe

- Place a small pink eraser in a brown bag. Pass the bag around the circle and ask children to use senses besides sight to discover what the object is.

- Record their guesses. Then open the bag and have them look inside. Ask: **What did you use to figure out what object it was?**

- Repeat throughout this unit, using different objects each time.

Singing Time

Sing *Use Your Senses* and *You Can Sort* with your class throughout this unit. As children sing along with the CD, they can use the posters to make a connection between the words they hear and the words on the page. They can also use the pictures to help them visualize the concept.

Eyes of all Colors

Objective: Learn that there are many different eye colors.

Science Inquiry Skills: observe, compare, classify

- Discuss with children how we use our eyes for our sense of sight. Explain that eyes come in different colors.

- Provide small groups with a hand mirror. Have children look at their eye color in the mirror.

- Ask children to use a crayon to color their eye color on an index card.

- Display cards by color and discuss which color has the most and which has the least.

Materials
- index cards
- crayons
- hand mirror

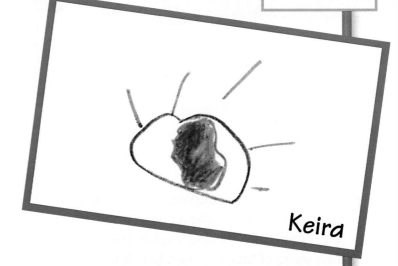

Keira

Looking Carefully

Objective: Notice changes in an array of objects.

Science Inquiry Skills: observe, compare, communicate

- Provide a tray with small objects on it. Have children look carefully at the things on the tray. Cover the objects with a piece of cloth and remove two objects.

- Remove the cloth and ask children to guess which items are missing. After each child has said what they think is missing, show the missing pieces.

- Repeat several times, removing a different number and type of object each time.

Materials
- tray
- small objects
- cloth

Using Our Five Senses

Objective: Children will learn about the five senses.

Get Started

- Ask: **What do you know about pumpkins?**

- As children answer, ask: **How do you know it is orange?** (Possible Answer: I can see it.) Explain that when we look at something we are using our sense of sight.

- If someone in the group describes cutting a pumpkin and cleaning it out, ask how it felt. When they respond, explain they used their sense of touch to learn how it felt.

Read a Picture

- Show children the photograph on page 1 of the Flipbook. Ask children to describe what they see.

- Now read the question on the Flipbook page. Ask: **What senses are the children using to learn about this pumpkin?** (touch, sight, smell)

- Ask children if they can hear a pumpkin. (Possible Answers: no, it doesn't talk; yes, if it falls it could make a loud noise)

What are they doing?

Science Facts

When you help children develop a heightened awareness of their senses, you are helping them to improve their observation skills. By asking them to describe how something feels, tastes, sounds, looks, or smells, you can help them learn new descriptive words. The more precise and comprehensive your students' vocabulary becomes, the greater their ability will be to communicate what they observe.

Reading in Science

- Learning how to look carefully at a photograph or picture and describe what they see is an important skill to develop in emergent readers.

- As they discuss the photograph, help children develop new vocabulary and learn how to organize their thoughts and communicate their ideas to others.

- Communicating is also one of the primary science inquiry skills.

✓ Informal Assessment

As you use the terms for the five senses, children will begin to learn what these terms mean, and eventually they will incorporate them into their own speaking vocabulary. Listen for proper use of these terms.

Finger Play

Five little pumpkins sitting on a gate
The first one said, "Oh my, it's getting late!"
The second one said, "I feel the wind in the air!"
The third one said, "I don't care!"
The fourth one said, "Let's run and run and run!"
The fifth one said, "I'm ready for some fun!"
Ooooo! Went the wind, and out went the light,
And the five little pumpkins, rolled out of sight.

More to Read

The Pumpkin Book, by Gail Gibbons
(Holiday House, 1999)
Help your students learn more about pumpkins by reading this book.

Activity   Use some of the recipes from this book with your class to explore both cooking and following a recipe.

Look Again

Objective: Children will learn to compare and observe closely.

Get Started

- Prepare Flipbook page 2 by covering the right hand photograph with a sheet of paper.

- Before showing children the Flipbook page, ask: **What do you know about farms?**

- Encourage children to use complete sentences when describing farms. Model this strategy as you rephrase the children's answers for the class.

Read a Picture

- Display Flipbook page 2 and point to the photograph on the left. Explain that after you talk together about this photograph, you will show them another photograph on the right side of the page.

- Encourage children to describe what they see, rephrasing what they tell you in complete sentences.

- Once the photograph has been discussed, remove the paper from the photograph on the right.

- Ask children what they notice about this photograph. Help them discuss how the two photographs are alike and different. (Possible Responses: In the second picture there is a cow, the man is gone, no silo, and 2 chickens.)

What do you see?

 Science Facts

The two nearly identical farm scenes will encourage children to look carefully at what is the same and what is different. Describing these two photographs will heighten your students' ability to observe and communicate what they see. It will also give you an opportunity to extend children's understanding of the relationship between plants and animals on a farm.

2

- Using complete sentences will help children understand how ideas are expressed.

- Discussing the Flipbook pages will help children develop more confidence in their ability to share ideas and information.

- Create a safe environment by accepting all answers.

✓ Informal Assessment

Observe children while they have Center Time or free play. Notice if children are using sentences to communicate their ideas and encourage them to do so throughout their day.

EL

Help English learners to obtain valuable vocabulary as you use the Flipbook page together. Point to each animal, ask them to name it in their native language and then provide the English word for them. Point to and name each animal and invite children to repeat after you.

More to Read

Farm Alphabet Book, by Jane Miller
(Scholastic, 1981)

Use this book for more information about life on a farm.

Activity Expose children to letters in the alphabet by making animal posters. Help children think of the names of animals that begin with the letter you are discussing and then have them draw these animals on the poster.

Sorting and Classifying

Objective: Children will learn to sort and classify objects.

Get Started

- Before discussing Flipbook page 3, show children a collection of buttons.

- Explain that you want them to help you sort the buttons into two categories: *buttons that are round* and *buttons that are not round*. Make two yarn circles (one red and one a different color).

- Pass the buttons around, giving everyone a chance to take a button from the container and decide whether it belongs in the round or not round group.

Read a Picture

- Using Flipbook page 3, cover the buttons that are not round with self-stick notes.

- Show children page 3 of the Flipbook. Ask: **What do all the buttons on this page have in common?** (they are round)

- Now remove the self-stick notes one at a time. Ask children to use words to describe each button (its shape, color, size, number of holes), and if it is like any of the round buttons.

- Continue until all the buttons have been uncovered.

Tell about these buttons.

 Science Facts

Helping children decide what belongs in a group and why it belongs is an important science process skill that can be reinforced during science time at the Math Center, and during story time. The buttons on this page can be sorted in many different ways: grouped by the number of holes, shape, size or color. Encourage children to explore all the different attributes of the buttons.

3

Reading in Science

- As you discuss the Flipbook page, encourage children to use position words (above, below, under, beside, next to) to describe the relative positions of the buttons.

- Remind them to use complete sentences as they describe the buttons.

✓ Informal Assessment

Work with small groups of children to discuss and sort buttons on the Flipbook page or with a button collection. As children sort, note who can sort into two groups and who has difficulty. Continue to provide multiple opportunities for children to sort materials, using one or more attributes.

EL

As you help children sort buttons, point out the common descriptive words such as round and blue. Then show English learners other objects that fit the same descriptive word. Point to the object and say the descriptive word. Then have children repeat the word after you.

More to Read

The Button Box, by Margarette S. Reid (Dutton 1990)

Activity Use this book for more practice with sorting and classifying buttons.

Predicting

Objective: Children will learn to predict events.

Get Started

- Ask children if they have ever played with blocks.

- Help them discuss what they have made, whether they played with them alone or with a friend.

- Discuss what happens when their block tower collapses. Ask: **What do you do when your block tower falls?**

Read a Picture

- Show children page 4 of the Flipbook. Ask children to describe what they see.

- Now read the question, pointing to the words as you read.

- Encourage children to discuss what might happen. When a child responds, ask: **Why do you think that might happen?** Help children learn to use information in the photograph to justify their predictions.

Flipbook
UNIT A • LESSON 4

What might happen next?

Science Facts

When young children build with blocks, they are discovering firsthand many things: what happens if you do not have a solid foundation for a building, that it is hard to balance blocks on top of a cylinder because they roll, that large blocks are heavier than small blocks, that two triangles placed together might be the same size as a small square block. As children build, be sure to talk with them about their buildings, and help them begin to verbalize what happened when their block tower collapsed – or why it did not.

Reading in Science

- When children listen to stories they begin to develop an understanding of cause and effect.

- Learning to predict an outcome based on information gathered from the text or illustration is an important skill young emergent readers need to develop.

- Encourage children to make predictions as you discuss the Flipbook page and stories you read throughout your day.

✓ Informal Assessment

Throughout the day, ask children to make predictions. Have them predict what might be for lunch, what the next activity might be, or what the weather might be like. Help children justify their predictions.

Take a Trip

Take a trip to your local park or playground. Find situations where children can predict what might happen including looking at leaves that may fall off trees or someone throwing away garbage in the trash can. When you return to the classroom, encourage children to discuss whether or not their predictions were correct.

More to Read

Do You Want To Be My Friend?, by Eric Carle (Putnam, 1988)

Activity Use this and other predictable books to help children predict what might happen next.

Observe and Assess

Use the Flipbook

Revisit the unit's Flipbook pages and discuss them with small groups of children. Assess children's ability to express their ideas and understanding of the material.

Use the Big Science Reader

Reread *What Do Scientists Do?* in the Big Science Reader, Vol. 1 with small groups. Assess children's ability to describe similarities and differences on pages 2 and 3.

Performance Assessment

If children are not yet able to sort objects into groups, give them multiple opportunities to practice sorting by one attribute with a small amount of objects.

Additional Activities

Go Further

More About Pumpkins

1. Revisit the pumpkin in the Science Center. Talk with children about how the pumpkin has changed over time. Revisit the predictions they made.

2. Show children the pumpkin that has been stored in the refrigerator. Ask: **What is different about this piece of pumpkin?**

3. Use this pumpkin to make pumpkin bread.

4. Be sure to communicate each step of the baking process with children.

Pumpkin Bread

Combine:

Pumpkin

$1\frac{1}{2}$ cups flour

$\frac{1}{4}$ tsp. salt

$\frac{1}{2}$ tablespoon baking powder

$\frac{1}{2}$ tsp. cinnamon

$\frac{1}{4}$ tsp. ground ginger

$\frac{1}{2}$ cup sugar

Beat together:

1 egg

$\frac{1}{2}$ cup milk

$\frac{1}{8}$ cup melted butter

Add to dry ingredients.

Stir until all ingredients are moistened. The batter will be lumpy. Pour into a greased loaf pan and bake at 350° for about 35 minutes, or until a toothpick inserted in the center of the loaf comes out dry.

School-to-Home

Be sure to send home the Home Letter from p. R2 with a list of books that your students can share with their families.

Start the Year   UNIT A • Be a Scientist

Dear Parents,

We are finishing up our first unit in science. We have looked at how cats are alike, how butterflies are different, how to sort buttons into groups, how to look carefully at things through a magnifying lens, how to predict what might happen next, and many more activities.

Here is a list of books that you can find at your local public library. You can read these books with your child to help reinforce what we are learning in class.

Brown Bear, Brown Bear, What Do You See?
by Bill Martin, Jr.
(Henry Holt & Co., 1996)

Have You Seen My Duckling?
by Nancy Tafuri
(Morrow, 1991)

My Spring Robin
by Anne Rockwell
(Simon & Schuster, 1996)

LOG ON www.macmillanmh.com for more science online.

Teacher's Notes

Unit Planner

Plants

Lesson	Objective	Resources
1 What Plants Need pp. 30–31	Children will learn what plants need to grow.	Flipbook, p. 5
2 Take a Closer Look pp. 32–33	Children will learn the parts of a plant, such as flowers, leaves, stem, and roots.	Flipbook, p. 6
3 All Kinds of Seeds pp. 34–35	Children will learn about various seeds and pits.	Flipbook, p. 7
4 Trees pp. 36–37	Children will learn to notice the different sizes and shapes of trees.	Flipbook, p. 8
5 Flowers pp. 38–39	Children will learn about different flower shapes, sizes, and colors.	Flipbook, p. 9
6 Plants We Eat pp. 40–41	Children will learn about plant parts that people eat.	Flipbook, p. 10

Flipbook

Use pages 5–10 to help children learn about different types of plants, how they grow and change, and how to observe the world carefully.

Big Science Reader

For Unit B, the story *Plants* exposes children to the different types of plants and plant environments. It allows children to explore the various attributes of flowers and trees including color, shape, and size.

Science Songs (CD and Posters)

You can use the songs, *What Plants Need* (tracks 5–6) and *Plants We Eat* (tracks 7–8) for an exciting way to learn about plants. Children can relate to how plants grow as they grow themselves. Use the posters, and have children sing along as they discover the world of plants.

Materials

Science Kit

- plastic growing containers
- hand lenses
- soil

Collectibles

- seeds, beans
- yarn
- zippered plastic bags
- paper towels
- vegetables
- leaves

From Seed to Plant, by Gail Gibbons
(Holiday House, 1993)

Explore a detailed and engaging explanation of the process of a plant's growth, from seed to sprout to fully developed plant with this book.

Growing Vegetable Soup, by Lois Ehlert
(Voyager Books, 1990)

A boy and his father grow vegetables in their garden and then use them to make soup. Various elements of gardening, including tools are illustrated.

Jack's Garden, by Henry Cole
(HarperTrophy, 1997)

This cumulative text, based on the rhyme "This is the house that Jack built," tells the story of Jack as he tends to a beautiful garden.

Planting a Rainbow, by Lois Ehlert
(Voyager Books, 1992)

This book describes the steps of planning and planting a garden, and includes bold and labeled illustrations of various flowers in their different stages of growth.

Tell Me, Tree, by Gail Gibbons
(Little Brown, 2002)

This informative book covers various topics regarding trees, including the parts of a tree, how trees grow, and different types of trees. It also includes sections on tree identification and the ways in which people, animals and the environment make use of trees.

The Tiny Seed, by Eric Carle
(Aladdin, 2001)

This story follows a tiny seed as it goes through the process of growing into a flower.

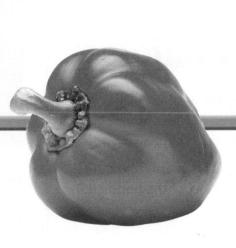

School-to-Home

Be sure to send home the Home Letter from p. R3 with an activity that your students can do with their families.

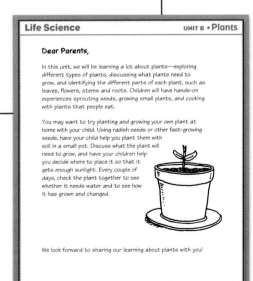

Life Science UNIT B • **Plants**

Dear Parents,

In this unit, we will be learning a lot about plants—exploring different types of plants, discussing what plants need to grow, and identifying the different parts of each plant, such as leaves, flowers, stems and roots. Children will have hands-on experiences sprouting seeds, growing small plants, and cooking with plants that people eat.

You may want to try planting and growing your own plant at home with your child. Using radish seeds or other fast-growing seeds, have your child help you plant them with soil in a small pot. Discuss what the plant will need to grow, and have your children help you decide where to place it so that it gets enough sunlight. Every couple of days, check the plant together to see whether it needs water and to see how it has grown and changed.

We look forward to sharing our learning about plants with you!

Bank Street For more information on these or other books, visit **www.bankstreetbooks.com** or your local library.

Plants

Plants are living things.

They grow and change.

Plants that need very little light live in shady places.

Plants that need a lot of light live in open fields.

Before Reading

- Ask children what they know about plants. Ask: **Does anyone have plants in their home? What do you like about plants?** (Accept all answers.)

- Show children the table of contents and model looking for the page number of the non-fiction selection, *Plants*.

During Reading

- After reading pp. 10–11, discuss what children notice about how the plant is changing. Encourage them to use descriptive language, such as *taller* or *bigger*.

- Using pp. 14–15, ask children to describe what is similar about trees and flowers. Record children's responses. (Possible Responses: they both grow in the ground; they both have leaves)

- Read the rest of the selection and discuss the plants that children see (or eat) everyday.

Did you know that trees are plants too?

14

Some plants have brightly colored flowers.

15

Some plants have parts that are good to eat!

16

After Reading

- Remind children what they discussed in Unit A about how scientists use their five senses to learn about their world.

- Show children a plant and ask them to look at it and describe what they notice.

- Explain that you will place the plant in the Science Center, where they can use their senses of smell and touch to learn even more about this plant.

- Encourage children to use a hand lens to look at the leaves of the plant.

Teacher Tip

Choose a plant with a strong fragrance, such as an herb or flower, so children will be able to make use of their sense of smell.

I Had a Tiny Seed

I had a tiny little seed.
I put it in soil,
And it sprouted roots.
I put it in the Sun,
And it started to grow.
I gave it some water,
And then it had leaves.

Suddenly it was a plant,
And not a tiny little seed.

17

Read the poem *I Had a Tiny Seed*, on page 17 in the Big Science Reader, vol. 1, inviting children to chime in on parts they remember. Discuss what happens as a plant grows.

Reread the poem throughout the unit. See page 31 in The Big Science Reader for more reading strategies.

Be a Scientist

 30 MINUTES WHOLE CLASS

Investigation

From Seed to Sprout

Objective: Observe what happens as a seed begins to turn into a plant.

Science Inquiry Skills: observe, predict, compare

Materials

- fast-growing seeds or beans, such as wheat berries, lima beans, mung beans or soybeans
- zippered bags
- paper towels

1 Observe Select three different kinds of beans or seeds. Show each kind of seed to the group and explain that they will be growing them in the Science Center. Provide them with hand lenses and have them describe what the seeds or beans look like.

2 Predict Work with small groups of children to place seeds in zippered bags with moist paper towels. Put one type of seed in each plastic bag. Label the bag with the name of the seed, and put them in a place with natural light. Ask children what they think might happen to the seeds.

3 Observe Have children use a hand lens to observe changes over time in color, shape and size.

4 Compare Ask: **Which type of seed grew the fastest? Which grew more slowly?**

centers

Math

How Long?

Objective: Use connecting cubes to measure the length of carrots.

Science Inquiry Skills: measure, compare

- Explain that there are some plants we eat and that carrots grow underground.
- Have children use connecting cubes to measure the length of each carrot. Help children count the amount of cubes used to measure each carrot.
- Help children place the carrots in size order. Encourage them to use size and position words, such as *longer*, *shorter* and *next to*.

Materials

- carrots of varying lengths with the tops still attached
- connecting cubes

Cooking

Fruit Salad

Objective: Explore types of plants we eat and learn about their different parts.

Science Inquiry Skills: observe

- Wash and dry the fruit. Have children look at each fruit and help them find where the fruit was attached to the plant. Ask if they have ever seen this fruit growing on a tree or in a garden.
- Help children cut up the softer fruits with a plastic knife. Have them describe what the inside of each fruit looks like pointing out the seeds and pits. Mix everything together in a bowl, eat, and enjoy!

Materials

- seasonal fruits such as apples, oranges, bananas, peaches
- plates
- bowl
- plastic knives

Games

Two of a Kind

Objective: Classify different parts or types of plants (trees, flowers, seeds, leaves, and vegetables).

Science Inquiry Skills: classify, compare

- Work with a small group of children to sort the Photo Cards into groups such as *trees, flowers, leaves*, etc.
- Discuss how items that are not an exact match can still belong in the same group.
- After discussing the photos, have children play a matching game where they turn the cards face down and look for exact matches.

Materials

- Photo Sorting Cards #11–20

broccoli   broccoli   iris   iris

Art

Flower Collages

Objective: Begin to understand the parts of a flower.

Science Inquiry Skills: make a model

- Tell children that they are going to make a collage of a flower. Ask: **What shape will your leaves be? What color will the flower petals be?**
- Help children tear or cut sheets of colored paper into leaf shapes. Show them how they can use the yarn to make the stem.
- Encourage children to glue the stems and leaves to a sheet of paper.

Materials

- colored construction paper
- pieces of green yarn
- glue
- scissors

Science Activities

Circle Time

WHOLE CLASS

Plant Parts

Objective: Identify the parts of edible plants that people eat.

Science Inquiry Skills: observe, infer, communicate

- Explain to children that all vegetables are plants.

- Show the group some fresh spinach and a head of lettuce. Ask if they can guess what part of the lettuce and spinach plants we eat. Explain that we eat the leaves of the plant.

- During the week, bring in vegetables that show other plant parts and explore them in the same way.

Materials

- a variety of vegetables that represent different plant parts, such as cauliflower/ broccoli (flowers), celery/asparagus (stems), lettuce/ spinach (leaves) and carrots/ radishes (roots)

Singing Time

Sing *What Plants Need* and *Plants We Eat* with your class throughout this unit. As children sing along with the CD, they can use the posters to make a connection between the words they hear and the words on the page. They can also use the illustrations to help them understand the concept.

Room to Grow

Objective: To observe and name the roots of a plant.

Science Inquiry Skills: observe, infer

- Gently remove the soil from the roots of the potted plants (or remove the sprouts from the zippered bags). Give each child a hand lens. Have them look closely at the roots and describe what they see.

- Ask which part of the plant they think should be in the soil (the root), and which part should be sticking out. Encourage them to tell why.

- Show children how to gently place the seedling in the pots with enough soil so that the roots are covered and the plant is supported.

Materials

- sprouted seeds from "Be a Scientist" activity (or small potted plants with roots)
- small flower pots
- soil
- hand lens

Sorting Leaves

Objective: Describe and sort leaves of different shapes and textures.

Science Inquiry Skills: observe, compare, communicate

- Have children spread leaves out on a table. Have them describe what the leaves look and feel like. Encourage them to use descriptive words such as pointy, round, rough, and smooth.

- Place two sheets of paper on the table. Ask children to sort the leaves, using different attributes such as ones that are pointy and ones that are round.

- Have children continue to sort the leaves using new sorting rules.

Materials

- leaves of different shapes
- sheets of paper

What Plants Need

Objective: Children will learn what plants need to grow.

Get Started

- Ask children if anyone has ever planted a seed or plant. Ask: **What did you have to do to take care of your plant?** (water it and give it light)

- Ask children where they think the light comes from. (the Sun) Ask: **How can plants get water?** (the rain or people watering them) Discuss the differences between plants that live inside and outside.

Read a Picture

- Show children the picture on page 5 of the Flipbook. Ask: **What are the people in this picture doing? What else do you see?** Encourage them to respond in full sentences.

- Read the question aloud. Encourage children to look carefully at the photograph. Ask: **What do you see in this picture that shows you what plants need to grow?**

- Ask what might happen if these people did not water the plants. (they might not survive, they might get water from rain)

What helps plants grow?

 ## Science Facts

Everything growing in the ground is a plant. Plants are living things. Plant leaves combine water, light, and the carbon dioxide in the air to make plant food. This process is called photosynthesis. Plant food is then carried from the leaves to the roots through a system of veins running through the plant. These same veins carry water up from the roots. In order to take in water and minerals, these roots need space to grow. After flowers die, they become fruits with seeds inside of them. Seeds can sprout into new plants.

5

Reading in Science

- After discussing the picture, reread the question, *What helps plants grow?* and ask children to help you count the number of words in the question.

- Run your finger under each word as they count.

- Then ask them to help you count how many letters are in each word.

- Have children tell you which word is the longest/shortest.

✔ Informal Assessment

Notice which children understand what plants need to grow. If children are having difficulty understanding this concept, have them help take care of plants in the classroom so they can understand what plants need to survive.

Finger Play

My Garden
This is my garden. I'll rake it with care.
And find some flower seeds that I'll plant
 right there.
The Sun will shine,
And the rain will fall,
And my flowers will blossom and grow
 straight and tall.

More to Read

Jack's Garden, by Henry Cole
(HarperTrophy, 1997)

This cumulative text, based on the rhyme "This is the house that Jack built," tells the story of Jack as he goes through the process of tending and growing a beautiful garden.

Activity   After reading this book together, have small groups act out the story (children can be flowers, plants, insects and birds) for the rest of the class.

Take a Closer Look

Objective: Children will learn the parts of a plant, such as flowers, leaves, stem, and roots.

Get Started

- Ask children to tell you what they know about plants. Encourage them to respond in full sentences.

- Show children a plant or picture of a plant and ask them to name the parts they know.

- Explain that if they do not know the correct name for a certain plant part, they can describe to you what it looks like (for example, the "long, skinny part" is the stem).

Read a Picture

- Cover the left side of Flipbook page 6. Show children the right side of the page, and ask them to describe what they see in each box.

- Uncover the left side of the page. Have children describe what they see in this picture. Explain that the boxes on the right side show what each part of the plant looks like close up.

- Point to each part of the plant on the left hand side and ask children to tell you the name of that part.

Plants have parts.

Science Facts

Flowers: A flower is the reproductive part of a plant. Its stamen makes pollen, and its pistil makes seeds. When pollen from the stamen gets into the pistil, pollination happens. Pollination is what makes new seeds.

Stems: Stems bring water, and minerals up from the roots, and carry plant food from the leaves down to the rest of the plant. Stems can also store food and water.

Leaves: Leaves combine light, water and carbon dioxide to make sugar. The sugar helps the plant grow. Leaves come in different colors and shapes; for example, a pine needle is a leaf, so is a round lily pad.

flower

stem

leaf

6

- After discussing the Flipbook page, reread the sentence, *Plants have parts*.

- Ask children if this is a sentence or a question. (a sentence) How do they know? (there is no question mark)

Informal Assessment

As you discuss the Flipbook pictures, take note of which children understand the different parts of a plant. Explain each plant part's function to help children remember them. Place a flowering plant in the Science Center for children to observe its plant parts.

Teacher Tip

As you discuss the concepts in this lesson, encourage children to make connections between their concrete experiences and the ideas you are exploring. Have them return to the various activities they have done with plants—such as sprouting or planting seedlings—and identify the different parts of those plants or sprouts.

More to Read

From Seed to Plant, by Gail Gibbons
(Holiday House, 1993)

This book provides a detailed and engaging explanation of the process of a plant's growth, from seed to sprout to fully developed plant.

Activity Cut out pieces of felt in the shape of leaves, stems, flowers, and roots. Have children choose one part from each pile and put them together to make a plant. Then have them change some or all of the parts to make a new plant.

All Kinds of Seeds

Objective: Children will learn about various seeds and pits.

Prepare: Bring in an avocado pit, some apple seeds in a sealed plastic bag, and some orange seeds in a separate sealed plastic bag.

Get Started

- Pass around the seeds. Ask children to describe the seeds. Record their responses.

- Ask: **What other foods have seeds? Why do you think fruits and vegetables have seeds?** (Possible Answers: because they are plants, so you can grow more of them)

Read a Picture

- Display Flipbook page 7 and point to each fruit asking children to identify each one. Encourage them to respond in full sentences. Model what they could say by providing a sentence frame, such as *That is a _____.*

- Ask: **Which plants have black seeds? Which plants have big seeds? Which plants have small seeds?**

- Ask: **Which plants have seeds on the inside? Which ones have seeds on the outside?** Have them use information from the picture to explain how they know this.

Where are the seeds?

strawberry

peach

orange

watermelon

Science Facts

A plant needs seeds in order to reproduce. The fruit is the part of a plant that makes seeds. It gives nourishment to the seeds until the seeds are ready to germinate and grow into new plants that can live on their own, making their own food.

Some fruits, like avocado, have only one seed inside of them. Others, like watermelon, have many. A strawberry has an average of 200 seeds that grow on the outside.

Inside of every seed is an embryo, a tiny basic copy of the plant. The embryo germinates—which means it will sprout and start growing into a new plant.

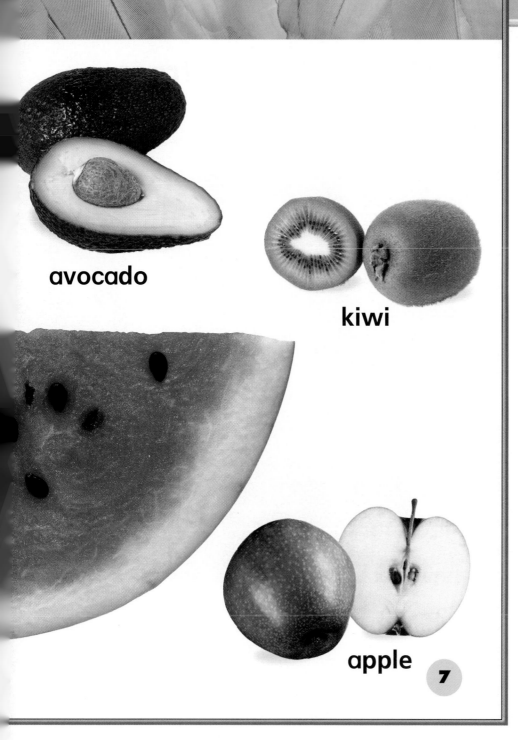

avocado

kiwi

apple

7

- Reread the question at the top of the Flipbook page. Point out the question mark. Ask children if they know what it is. Explain that a question always ends with a question mark.

- Invite a volunteer to point to the question mark on the page. Point out question marks as you read other selections to the class.

✓ Informal Assessment

If children are having difficulty pointing out the seeds in the picture, provide real seeds for children to explore and match to the seeds in the picture.

 ## Teacher Tip

If children are curious about what is inside seeds, you can soak some lima beans in water overnight, and then have children open them up and use hand lenses to examine the insides more closely. Ask them to describe what they see.

 ## More to Read

The Tiny Seed, by Eric Carle
(Aladdin, 2001)

In this story, a tiny seed faces adventures and challenges as it goes through the step-by-step process of growing into a flower.

Activity　Have children help you recall the order things happened in the story. Record their responses on large index cards using pictures and simple words. Then have children put the cards in order.

Trees

Objective: Children will learn to notice the different sizes and shapes of trees.

Get Started

- Ask children to tell you about trees they see near their home or school. Ask: **What do the trees look like? Do they all look the same?**

- Tell children that you are going to draw a picture of a tree. Ask children to help you remember the parts of the tree as you draw it.

Read a Picture

- Show children page 8 of the Flipbook. Ask: **What do you notice about all these trees?** As children describe a particular tree, encourage them to use descriptive words, such as pointy and skinny, to identify which tree they are referring to.

- Ask: **How are these trees alike?** (Possible Answers: they all have trunks; they are tall; they are plants)

- Ask children to look at the leaves on the trees. Help them describe the shape, size and color of the leaves.

- Point to the picture of the palm tree. Ask children what is different about this tree than the other two trees. (it grows in the sand, its trunk is skinny)

Tell about these trees.

Science Facts

The first tree is an evergreen. Evergreens are conifers or trees that produce cones. They stay green all year, losing their leaves little by little. The leaves are slowly replaced at the same time, so they never have bare branches.

The second tree is an English Oak. It is a deciduous tree or a tree that loses its leaves before the winter. In the fall, as leaves of deciduous trees die, the colors that were hidden under the green begin to show themselves. The leaves also make new colors.

The last tree is a palm tree. Palm trees usually grow in tropical climates that are wet and warm.

8

- After discussing the trees on the page, go back and reread the sentence, *Tell about these trees.*

- Ask children if this is a question. (No, it is a sentence.) **How do you know?** (It does not have a question mark.)

✔ Informal Assessment

It may take a while for some children to recognize that there are many different kinds of trees. Help them look at additional pictures of trees and encourage them to identify and describe the parts that are different from each other. (color of the bark, shape of the leaves)

Take a Trip

Take a walk to look for trees. Bring a tree identification book to help identify trees you see. Encourage children to search on the ground to collect leaves that may have fallen from the trees, and bring these back to the classroom. When you return to the classroom, provide an opportunity for children to share the leaves they collected with the class. Encourage children to talk about how their leaves are the same and/or different.

More to Read

Tell Me, Tree, by Gail Gibbons
(Little Brown, 2002)

This excellent book about trees will reinforce and extend children's understanding of trees.

Activity   Use the leaves that children collect from outside to make leaf rubbings. Have children place a sheet of paper over their leaf and rub a crayon over it.

Flowers

Objective: Children will learn about different flower shapes, sizes, and colors.

Get Started

- Ask children to tell you what they know about flowers. Record their responses on a chart labeled *What we know about flowers.*

- Ask children to describe where they have seen flowers. (Possible Answers: grocery store, flower shop, gardens, park)

- If any of the children have planted flowers, have them tell what they did.

Read a Picture

- Show children page 9 of the Flipbook. Ask them to tell about the flowers. Encourage them to use position words, such as on the top, on the bottom, and next to as they refer to each flower. Help children identify the color of each flower. As they describe each flower, point to it and read the label.

- Explain that even though many flowers look different from each other, they all have the same basic parts (stem, leaves, petals). Help children to find plant parts on each picture.

What colors are these flower

carnation

rose

lilac

Science Facts

Flowers have petals, sepals, carpels (the parts that make seeds) and stamens (the parts that make pollen). Colorful, strong-smelling flowers attract bees and other insects, who carry the flowers' pollen to other flowers. Small flowers that don't have a strong smell rely on wind to transport pollen.

Some tree flowers, like orange blossoms, develop into fruit that we eat. Others, like lilacs, do not. Many flowers, such as tulips, are cultivated because they are attractive and colorful. There are almost 2,000 kinds of tulips, and they come in every color except blue and black.

daisy

tulip

orange blossom

⑨

- After discussing the flowers, point to the words by the flowers and ask children to tell you what all these words are. (labels)

- Remind children that labels give you information about the pictures they describe.

✓ Informal Assessment

Have groups of children look at page 9 of the Flipbook. Ask children to identify the parts of a flower and point to each part. If children are having difficulty, bring in a real flower and review the parts.

EL

Have English learners look at the flowers on Flipbook page 9. Point to each flower and model naming its color by using the following frame: (*color word*) *flower*. For example, say: *red flower*. Invite children to repeat after you. Then model using a complete sentence. For example, *The flower is red*. Invite children to repeat after you.

More to Read

Planting a Rainbow, by Lois Ehlert
(Voyager Books, 1992)

This book describes the steps of planning and planting a garden, and includes labeled illustrations of flowers in their different stages of growth.

Activity   Encourage children to draw flowers when they work at the Drawing and Writing Center.

Plants We Eat

Objective: Children will learn about plant parts that people eat.

Prepare: Bring in a pepper, a cucumber, and a vegetable peeler.

Get Started

- Ask children to name some plants that we eat. Record their responses.

- Show children the vegetables you have brought to school. Point out where the cucumber and peppers were once attached to the stem. Pass them around so each child can examine that spot.

Read a Picture

- Show children page 10 of the Flipbook. Point to the salad and ask children what it is. Ask children if they like to eat salad and have them tell what they like in a salad.

- Help children identify the different vegetables by reading the label and asking them to tell about the color and shape of each one.

- Explain which part of the plant we eat. Ask: **Why do you think it is important to wash plants before eating them?** (to remove the dirt, to wash away germs)

- Explain that some plants have an outer layer that is usually removed before eating it. Show children the vegetable peeler and use it to peel the cucumber. Pass around a piece of the skin. Have children tell how it feels. Share the cucumber with children who want a taste. Be aware of any allergies children may have.

Which plants do you eat?

peppers

onion

lettuce

Science Facts

Botanists, people who study plants, call many of our "vegetables" fruits. That is because they classify fruit as anything that contains its own seeds. For example, botanists consider tomatoes, peas, peppers and cucumbers to be fruits. Other "vegetables" fall into surprising categories. Broccoli is the flowering part of a plant; when we eat broccoli, we are eating a flower. When we eat lettuce, we are eating a plant's leaves. Celery is a plant's stem. We also eat plant roots, like carrots and radishes. They taste sweet because they store sugar that their plant uses to grow its leaves and flowers. They are pulled out of the ground before the leaves and flowers can grow.

mushroom

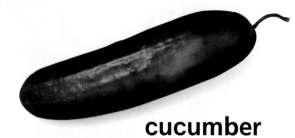

cucumber

tomatoes

10

- Point to the labels and ask children to tell what these words are.

- Ask: **How do these labels help us understand what is on the page?** Have volunteers read the labels they know or point out letters they know.

- Encourage children to assign different descriptive labels to the pictures, such as *green* or *red*.

Informal Assessment

Show children pictures of different plants, some that are edible and some that are not. Ask children to tell you which plants people can eat.

Take a Trip

Arrange to take your class to a farmer's market or grocery store. Discuss how we buy our fruits and vegetables from a market, but they originally come from farms. You can buy the ingredients for a class salad while you are there. When you return to the classroom, have children help to make a salad. As you make the salad, discuss the what vegetables you are putting in and what part of the plant it is.

More to Read

Growing Vegetable Soup, by Lois Ehlert (Voyager Books, 1990)

A boy and his father grow vegetables and use them to make soup. This book's colorful illustrations include plants and gardening tools.

Activity If possible make vegetable soup. Have children help you clean and cut vegetables for your soup. Write the recipe on chart paper so children can use it to recall each step.

Observe and Assess

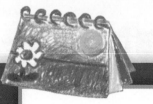

Use the Flipbook

Revisit the unit's Flipbook pages and discuss them with small groups of children. Assess children's ability to express their understanding of different types of plants and their parts.

Use the Big Science Reader

Reread *Plants* in the Big Science Reader, vol. 1 with small groups. Assess children's ability to describe how plants grow and change, and to provide examples of different kinds of plants.

Performance Assessment

If children do not yet seem to recognize the attributes that make something a plant, continue to play games with the Photo Sorting Cards to give them more experience with different types of plants and their parts.

oak tree

tulip

oak leaf

watermelon seeds

lettuce

Go Further

More About Sprouts

1 Revisit the sprouts in the Science Center. Talk with children about how the sprouts have changed over time.

2 Explain that sprouts are also a kind of plant that some people like to eat. Have a sprout tasting party where you bring in sprouts and put them in a salad for all to taste. Be aware of any allergies children may have.

3 Make a chart of who liked the sprouts and who did not.

School-to-Home

Be sure to send home the Home Letter from p. R4 with a list of books that your students can share with their families.

Life Science   UNIT B • Plants

Dear Parents,

We are finishing up our unit in science about plants. We have looked at what plants need to grow, various types of plants, the plants that people eat, and the different parts of plants. We have sprouted seeds, planted seedlings and looked closely at the parts of a plant.

Here is a list of books you can find at your local public library. You can read these books to your child to help reinforce what we are learning in class.

Growing Vegetable Soup
by Lois Ehlert
(Voyager Books, 1990)

Jack's Garden
by Henry Cole
(HarperTrophy, 1997)

The Tiny Seed
by Eric Carle
(Aladdin, 2001)

 www.macmillanmh.com for more science online.

Teacher's Notes

Unit Planner

Animals

Lesson	Objective	Resources
1 What Animals Need pp. 54–55	Children will learn what animals need to live.	Flipbook, p. 11
2 Grow and Change pp. 56–57	Children will learn how animals grow and change.	Flipbook, p. 12
3 Baby Animals pp. 58–59	Children will learn how adult animals care for their offspring.	Flipbook, p. 13
4 Insects pp. 60–61	Children will identify and compare insects.	Flipbook, p. 14
5 Birds pp. 62–63	Children will learn characteristics of birds.	Flipbook, p. 15
6 Water Animals pp. 64–65	Children will learn about animals that live in the ocean.	Flipbook, p. 16
7 Living Together pp. 66–67	Children will learn how plants and animals live together.	Flipbook, p. 17

Flipbook

Use pages 11–17 to help children learn about the different types of animals there are, how they grow and change, and how plants and animals live together.

Big Science Reader

For Unit C, the story, *Animals,* exposes children to the different ways animals eat, hide, and look. It allows children to explore the various attributes of animals including color, shape, and size.

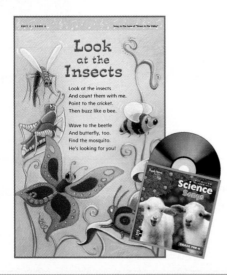

Science Songs (CD and Posters)

You can use the songs *Watch Us Grow* (tracks 9–10) and *Look at the Insects* (tracks 11–12) for an exciting way to learn about animals. Children can make the sounds and pretend they are different animals. Use the posters and have children sing along as they discover the world of animals.

Materials

Science Kit

- plastic container
- mesh pieces
- soil

Collectibles

- plastic spoons
- food scraps
- small stones and sticks
- books about animals

Unit Bibliography

A Hummingbird's Life, by John Himmelman
(Children's Press, 2000)

This book shows what hummingbirds eat, how they feed their babies, and what they do when it gets cold.

Are You a Grasshopper?, by Judy Allen and Tudor Humphries
(Kingfisher, 2002)

This book discusses the life cycle of a grasshopper.

Are You a Snail?, by Judy Allen and Tudor Humphries (Kingfisher, 2000)

This book invites children to think of themselves as snails. Children will see detailed drawings and learn interesting snail facts.

Baby's World: Baby Animals
(DK Publishing, Inc., 2002)

This book illustrates a variety of baby animals.

From Egg to Robin, by Susan Canizares
(Scholastic, 1998)

This book uses close-up photos to show children how baby robins hatch from eggs and what they look like as they grow.

Hermit Crabs, by Lola M. Schaefer
(Heinemann Library, 2002)

Clear photographs of hermit crabs help children learn what they look like, as well as how crabs move, eat and have babies.

Make Way for Ducklings, by Robert McCloskey
(Viking, 1976)

This classic fiction story tells about how Mr. and Mrs. Mallard find a place to raise their baby ducklings in the middle of Boston.

Polar Bear, Polar Bear, What Do You Hear?
by Bill Martin Jr./Eric Carle
(Henry Holt, 1991)

Children can learn about and imitate different animal sounds as they read this book about animal noises.

Snails, by Monica Hughes
(Raintree, 2004)

With bright, clear photographs and simple text, this book conveys information about snails.

The Journey of a Swallow, by Carolyn Scrace
(Franklin Watts, 2000)

How do baby swallows grow into adults? This book follows a swallow over the course of its life.

The New Puppy, by Anne Civardi
(Usborne, 2001)

Children can learn how people care for a new puppy as they follow the Applebys and "Shrimp," the new canine member of their family.

School-to-Home

Be sure to send home the Home Letter from p. R5 with an activity that your students can do with their families.

Bank Street
For more information on these or other books, visit **www.bankstreetbooks.com** or your local library.

Life Science   UNIT C • Animals

Dear Parents,

For our next science unit the children will be learning about animals. We will talk about what animals need to survive—food, air, water and shelter—and about how they grow. The children will learn about different kinds of animals, including birds, insects and water animals.

Find opportunities to talk with your child about animals. If you have a pet, talk with your child about what your family does to take care of it. Ask questions such as, What does your pet eat? Where does it sleep? How do you take care of your pet if it gets sick? If you do not have a pet, you can visit a friend who does, or take your child to the petting zoo or a local farm.

We look forward to sharing our learning about animals with you!

Big Science Reader

Before Reading

- Ask: **What animals can you think of that are bigger than you? Smaller than you?**

- Record children's answers in two lists: *Big Animals* and *Small Animals*.

- Model using the table of contents, to find the page number for *Animals*.

During Reading

- As you read, give children time to discuss and name the animals that appear on each page.

- On page 20, ask: **Why do you think an animal might need to stay safe?** (Accept all answers.)

- On page 23, have children discuss how the frogs are the same and different.

- On page 26, ask: **How do we know that something is alive?**

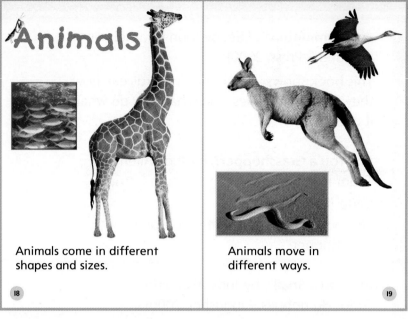

Animals

Animals come in different shapes and sizes.

18

Animals move in different ways.

19

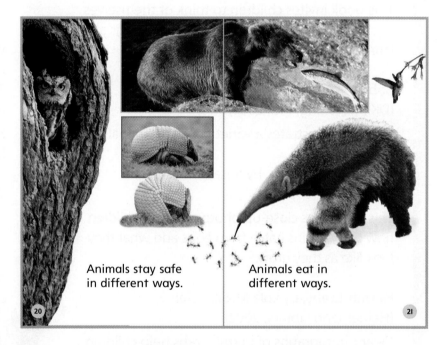

Animals stay safe in different ways.

20

Animals eat in different ways.

21

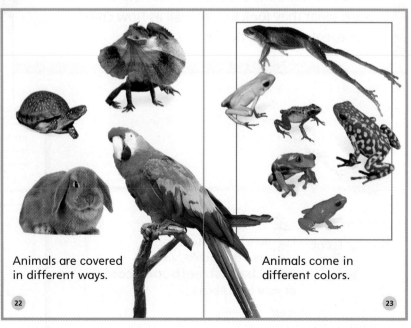

Animals are covered in different ways.

22

Animals come in different colors.

23

Animals live in different places.

But there is one way all animals are alike.

24   25

They are
alive!

26

- Go back to the lists of big and small animals that you made.

- Ask children if they want to add more animals to the lists.

Animals, Animals Everywhere

Animals, animals everywhere!
Some are big
And some are small.
And some are in between.

Animals, animals everywhere!
Some swing from the trees,
And some swim in the sea.

Animals, animals everywhere!
Some are blue
And some are brown,
And some are even green.

27

Read the poem, *Animals, Animals Everywhere,* on page 27 of the Big Science Reader, Vol. 1.

Reread the poem, inviting children to join in on parts they remember. See page 31 for more reading strategies.

Read this poem throughout the unit.

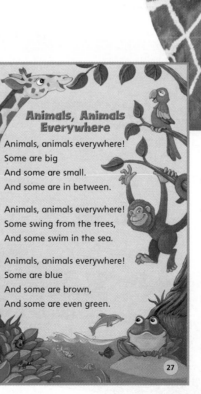

Be a Scientist

 15 MINUTES **WHOLE CLASS** **Investigation**

Observing Animals

Objective: Make a snail habitat that can be observed over time.

Science Inquiry Skills: infer, observe, communicate

1 **Infer** Ask: **What do you think snails need in order to live? What would we need to create a home for them in the classroom?**

2 Have children feed and water the snails each day.

3 **Observe** Have children observe the snails throughout the unit. Ask: **How do they move? How can they climb up the side of the tank? How does it feel when the snail moves on your hand? Why do they go inside their shells?**

4 **Communicate** Record children's observations of the snail. To help children learn to draw the snails, ask: **What shape is the snail's shell? What shape is its body?** You can also provide a snail diagram in the Science Center for children to use as a reference.

Materials

- snails
- mesh (for a lid)
- clear plastic tank or container
- soil, small stones and sticks
- tape
- food (kale, lettuce, carrots)
- egg shells
- spoon

centers

Dramatic Play

Materials
- pet care items

Pet Play

Objective: Recognize how people care for pets.

Science Inquiry Skills: communicate, infer

- Gather objects that can be used to care for pets, such as, empty food boxes and dishes.

- Before Center Time, ask the group to describe how they care for pets at home. Show them the new props.

- Encourage children to pretend to be pets and pet owners. Ask: **What might pet owners do? How can the "pets" communicate with their owners?**

Puzzles

Materials
- various animal puzzles

Animal Puzzles

Objective: Work together on animal puzzles.

Science Inquiry Skills: communicate, infer

- During Circle Time, show children the animal puzzles. Invite children to tell what they know about each animal they see.

- Encourage children to work together on these puzzles during Center Time.

Blocks

Materials
- toy animals

Building a Farm

Objective: Use blocks to create shelter for farm animals.

Science Inquiry Skills: make a model

- At Circle Time, show children plastic farm animals or help children draw farm animals and explain that you will add them to the Block Area.

- Ask: **What kinds of buildings are on a farm? What animals might live in a barn? In a field? Why do farm fields have fences?**

- During Block Time, encourage children to build structures for the animals.

Library

Materials
- books about animals

Book Look

Objective: Explore informational books about animals.

Science Inquiry Skills: observe, communicate

- Collect animal books and place them in a special basket so that children can find the books easily.

- At Circle Time, hold up the books and tell children they will be in the Library Center.

- Encourage children to look at the books with a partner and name the animals they see.

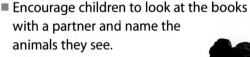 

Science Activities

Circle Time

WHOLE CLASS

Materials
- Photo Sorting Cards #21-40
- yarn or masking tape

Four Legs or Not?

Objective: Learn how to sort animals based on observable characteristics.

Science Inquiry Skills: compare, classify

- Make two yarn or tape circles in the center of your Circle Time area and explain one circle is for *animals with four legs* and the other is for *animals that do not have four legs.*

- Give each child a Photo Sorting Card and have them decide which circle it belongs in.

- Repeat throughout this unit, using other sorting rules such as *animals with* and *without wings* and *animals that live in water* and *animals that do not live in water.*

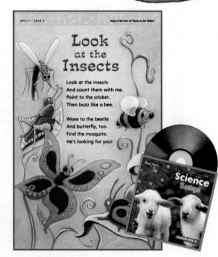

Singing Time

Sing *Watch Us Grow* and *Look at the Insects* with your class throughout this unit. Children can sing along with the CD and use the posters to learn more about people and animals.

Find a Match

Materials
- Photo Sorting Cards #21-40

Objective: Develop science vocabulary.

Science Inquiry Skills: classify

- Gather the Photo Sorting Cards and place them face-up in rows so that matches are set apart. Invite children in your small group to take turns finding the Photo Sorting Cards that are a match, placing the matches in a pile.

- As children pick up the cards, help reinforce the names of the animals by saying them aloud.

- Extend this activity by having children match the adult animal to its baby. Explain that some of the baby animals have the same name. Ask children if they know children who share the same name.

More About Classroom Animals

Materials
- your classroom animals in tank
- food scraps such as apple, cucumber, lettuce, carrot

Objective: Learn more about classroom animals through observation and inference.

Science Inquiry Skills: observe, infer

- Talk with children about what the animals have been eating. Ask: **What else do you think they might like to eat? Why?**

- Ask: **How can we find out if they like to eat those things?**

- Experiment with adding a different food to the tank. Have children observe the tank to see if the animals are eating the foods. Have them share their observations and record them on chart paper.

What Animals Need

Objective: Children will learn what animals need to live.

Get Started

- Ask: **What do animals need to stay alive? How do you know? Do animals need the same things we do?**

Read a Picture

- Show children the photograph on page 11 of the Flipbook. Ask children to describe what they see.

- Ask if anyone has a guinea pig at home. **How is it the same or different from the one in the picture? How is your guinea pig's cage the same or different from the one in the picture?**

- Ask: **What can we learn about guinea pigs by looking at this picture? How do you think it would feel if you were to touch the guinea pig? Why do you think some animals have fur?**

- Help children name the items in the tank and what each item is used for. (water bottle; food bowl; food ball)

Flipbook

UNIT C • LESSON 1

What do animals need?

Science Facts

Guinea pigs are part of the rodent family. Other rodents are rabbits, beavers, rats, squirrels, mice, and porcupines. Rodents are animals that use their two front teeth to gnaw on vegetables, the only food that they eat. The two front teeth get worn down from gnawing, but continue to grow throughout the rodent's life. A pet guinea pig needs to eat hard food that will allow it to grind down its teeth as if it is in the wild. Guinea pigs enjoy gnawing on carrots, celery, and cauliflower stalks.

Reading in Science

- Help children count the number of words in the question. (4)

- Next, help children count the number of letters in each word.

- Ask: **Which word is the longest?** (animals) **Which word is the shortest?** (do)

✓ Informal Assessment

When children discuss animal needs, note who has pets at home and is familiar with how to care for animals, and who does not. Children will learn more about what animals need as they care for the classroom pets.

Teacher Tip

The more animals you have in your classroom, the more children will be able to learn first hand what animals need in order to survive. Some easy classroom pets are: cold water fish, water snails, worms (easy to find and easy to draw), mealworms (children can see the life cycle – from worm to beetle), and small animals available at your local pet store, like salamanders, guinea pigs, hamsters, and gerbils.

More to Read

The New Puppy, by Anne Civardi (Usborne, 2001)
In this book, the Appleby family learns how to care for their new puppy.

Activity Ask children to list all the things puppies need. Create a word web to record children's responses.

Grow and Change

Objective: Children will learn how animals grow and change.

Get Started

- Say: **We are about to look at pictures of cats. Before we do, let's think about what we know about cats.**

- Have children share what they know and record their responses on chart paper.

- Ask: **Do you think kittens can do all these things when they are born? How do you think they change as they grow?**

Read a Picture

- Show children page 12 of the Flipbook. Read the question: *How does this cat grow and change?* Have children describe what they see at each stage.

- Next, have children talk about what stays the same as the cat gets bigger. For example, its nose is still pink and it still has fur.

- Ask: **What do you think this cat needs in order to grow up healthy?**
  (food, water, a home)

How does this cat grow and change?

just born

baby kitten

kitten

Science Facts

Kittens are born with their eyes closed, and it takes a week or two for them to open. At first, kittens sleep almost all of the time. They do not have teeth and do not need them, because they drink their mother's milk. At around two weeks, kittens begin to stand up. At four weeks, their teeth start coming in. They stop nursing, and begin drinking cow's milk from a saucer and eating canned kitten food. By this time, they are also able to begin to run and play.

full grown cat 12

- Write the word *cat* on the board and ask what letter this word begins with.

- Then ask if anyone's name begins with the same letter.

- Generate a list with children of other words that begin with *c*.

- Ask children if *cat* is a long or short word.

✓ Informal Assessment

If children have trouble identifying how baby animals grow and change, have them think of ways they have changed since they were babies. Then help them make the connection between how they changed and how animals change over time.

EL

Help EL students learn the names of animals by working with the Photo Sorting Cards #21–40. Show each picture and then read each animal name. Have children repeat each animal name as they point to each picture. You can also have children play a picture matching game with the Photo Sorting Cards. When children find two matching cards, encourage them to name the animal. Model the process and have children repeat after you.

More to Read

Baby's World: Baby Animals
(DK Publishing, Inc., 2002)

This book will help children distinguish between different animal babies.

Activity Think of some riddles that children can answer based on the information in the book. For example, I have four legs, and white wool, just like my mother. Who am I? (a lamb)

Baby Animals

Objective: Children will learn how adult animals care for their offspring.

Get Started

- Cover each picture on Flipbook page 13 with separate sheets of paper.

- Before discussing the Flipbook, ask: **What do you think baby animals need to learn how to do?** (Accept all responses.)

Read a Picture

- Using Flipbook page 13 remove the sheet of paper covering the lions.

- Read the question at the top of the Flipbook page. Then ask: **How is the grown-up lion caring for the cub?** (It is carrying it in its mouth.)

- Remove the paper covering the cows. Ask: **What do you think the cow is doing with her calf?** (Accept all responses.)

- Repeat for the last photograph. Ask: **How is the grown-up duck caring for the ducklings?** (She is leading her ducklings.)

- Ask: **How are the babies like their parents? How are they different?**

How do animals care for their babies?

 ## Science Facts

Cows usually give birth to one calf each year. A newborn calf can weigh 50 to 100 pounds, and can walk around soon after it is born. The calf gets milk from its mother.

Ducklings can feed themselves as soon as they get to the water, but must learn what is okay to eat. Back in the nest at night, their mother keeps them warm while they sleep.

A mother lion carries her babies by the scruff of the neck, the way a housecat carries kittens. Mother lions often help take care of each other's babies.

13

Reading in Science

- As children learn the names of the letters in their names, you can help them begin to recognize those same letters in other words.

- In this lesson, focus on the initial letter in each word.

- Point to an initial letter in a word, and ask if anyone's name begins with this letter.

✔ Informal Assessment

If children have trouble describing how grown-up animals care for their babies, have them think about how they are cared for by their parents or caregivers.

Finger Play

Slowly, slowly, very slowly (walk fingers up arm)
Creeps the garden snail.
Slowly, slowly, very slowly
Up the wooden rail.
Quickly, quickly, very quickly (run fingers up arm)
Runs the little mouse.
Quickly, quickly, very quickly
Round about the house.

More to Read

From Egg to Robin, by Susan Canizares (Scholastic, 1998)

This book describes how robins hatch from eggs and how they grow.

Activity Point out that baby birds start small and grow. Have children organize a set of objects from smallest to largest.

Insects

Objective: Children will identify and compare insects.

Get Started

- Start the meeting by making a very quiet, "Bzzzz" sound. Invite children to make the same sound. Ask: **What animal makes this sound?** They may say a fly or a bee or a mosquito. Tell children that these are insects.

- Remind children that they have been learning about animals that have *two* legs and *four* legs, but that an insect has *six* legs. Ask: **How many legs do we have?**

Read a Picture

- Show Flipbook page 14, covering each insect except for the ladybug with a self-stick note.

- Read the label for the ladybug. Ask: **What do you notice about this insect?**

- Then uncover the bee. Read the label. Ask: **What do you notice about this insect? How are these two alike? What is different?**

- Continue uncovering insects and asking children to talk about what they notice including similarities and differences among all of the insects.

Tell about these insects.

ladybug

bee

fly

butterfly

Science Facts

Ladybugs eat insects that attack plants, so many farmers use them to protect plants.

A bee's buzz is the sound of its fanning wings.

Only female mosquitoes bite, using the protein they get in order to produce eggs.

Beetles have two pairs of wings, but one pair is only for protection.

Flies spit on their food to soften it and then eat it.

A butterfly tastes food with its feet.

Ants can lift twenty times their own weight.

A grasshopper can leap twenty times the length of its own body.

mosquito

beetle

ant

grasshopper

14

- Learning to read labels is an important part of reading non-fiction selections.

- Point to the different words below each picture on Flipbook page 14. Remind children that these words are called labels and that labels help name or describe something in a picture.

- Read each label to children and ask them to tell what the labels do on this page. (They name each insect.)

✓ Informal Assessment

In groups, show children page 14 in the Flipbook again. Ask them to describe the attributes of insects (6 legs, they have wings, some are colorful). Notice who can describe the insects and who cannot. Help those who are struggling by describing the different insects for them.

Take a Trip

Go to a park or playground and have children look for insects by carefully turning over rocks and sticks and noticing plants and trees. Take along a field guide to help with identification. Discuss how to treat the insects so they do not get hurt. When you return to the classroom, invite children to draw pictures of the insects they found and tell about them.

More to Read

Are You a Grasshopper? by Judy Allen and Tudor Humphries (Kingfisher, 2002)

This book describes how grasshoppers are born and the stages of development.

Activity After reading the book, show children the illustrations and have them describe what happens as grasshoppers grow. Record their ideas on chart paper.

Birds

Objective: Children will learn characteristics of birds.

Get Started

- Say: **Guess who I am. I have feet but not arms. I have feathers. I have wings. Who am I?** (a bird)

- Ask children what else they know about birds. Record their responses on chart paper.

Read a Picture

- Ask: **What do you notice about these birds?** Encourage children to notice the colors of the birds and how they use their bodies in the pictures.

- Have children talk about what is the same among the birds (they all have beaks and feathers) and what is different. (sizes, colors, what they are doing)

- Point to the pelican. Ask children what they think it is doing. (eating) Then ask what they think he might be eating. (a fish) Ask them to tell how they know.

- Invite a volunteer to point to the bird that is flying. Then have a volunteer point to the bird that is feeding its babies.

What are these birds doing?

warbler

pelican

Science Facts

Eagles can see things that are one and half miles away, which helps them find their food and catch it.

Woodpeckers have hard, pointed beaks that they use to search for insects and to communicate with each other by tapping.

Hummingbirds hover while eating. Their beak and tongue are thin and long enough to get inside of flowers to lick up nectar.

A pelican's pouch is actually a fold of skin that gets wider as the pelican dives underwater to catch a fish.

Warblers often end up raising the babies of Cowbirds, who lay their eggs in warbler nests.

eagle

woodpecker

hummingbird

15

- Read each label to children.

- Ask children what these words are called.

- Have children think of alternative labels such as small or long-beaked.

- Ask children to identify the letters that they recognize on the page.

✓ Informal Assessment

Ask children to describe what a bird might look like to someone who has not seen a bird before. Notice if children are including wings, feathers and beaks in their descriptions.

Take a Trip

Go to a park or playground and have children look for birds. Encourage them to observe what the birds do. Ask: **Where were the birds? Did you see more than one kind of bird? What were the birds doing?** When you return to the classroom, invite children to act out different things they saw the birds doing. Encourage children to look out for birds when they are at home.

More to Read

A Hummingbird's Life, by John Himmelman (Children's Press, 2000)

The Journey of a Swallow, by Carolyn Scrace (Franklin Watts, 2000)

Each book describes a particular type of bird.

Activity Help groups of children choose which bird to make (swallow or hummingbird). Provide materials for children to make the body, wings, and beak.

Water Animals

Objective: Children will learn about animals that live in the ocean.

Get Started

- Ask children if they have ever been to the beach. Ask them to describe the different areas at the beach. (sand, ocean)

- Explain that some animals live in the ocean. Ask: **What are some animals that live in the ocean?**

- Record children's responses on chart paper.

Read a Picture

- Show children Flipbook page 16. Read the question, pointing to the words as you read. Ask children to describe what they see.

- Repeat children's observations, using the names of the ocean animals.

- Explain that some animals in the ocean are special because they need to come up for air unlike fish.

- Ask: **How are these animals the same? How are they different?**

Flipbook

UNIT C • LESSON 6

These animals live in water.

sea otter

seahorse

dolphins

Science Facts

Sea otters are one of the only groups of animals that use tools. Sea otters use small rocks to pry the abalone off of larger rocks and then break open the shells.

Sea horses pick one mate for life. Each morning, the male and female twirl around with their tails linked. Then they separate for the rest of the day. When they have babies, the male sea horse gets pregnant.

Dolphins are mammals, so they breathe air. They come to the surface to breathe through a blowhole on top of their heads about every two minutes.

fish

16

- Point to the word by each picture and ask what it is. (a label)

- Ask volunteers to read any labels they know using the pictures to help them.

- Help children think of alternative labels, such as yellow or furry.

✓ Informal Assessment

If children call every animal that lives in the water a fish, help them learn the names of other animals. You can do this by playing a matching game with the Photo Sorting Cards or looking together at books that describe a variety of water animals.

Teacher Tip

A classroom fish tank allows children to observe fish close up and over time. Goldfish are easy to maintain (you do not need a heater for the tank). If you have land snails in your Science Center, you could add water snails to your fish tank and help children learn about the two types of snails.

More to Read

Hermit Crabs, by Lola M. Schaefer (Heinemann Library, 2002)

Sea Horses, by Lola M. Schaefer (Heinemann Library, 2002)

These books describe water animals.

Activity   After reading these two books have children describe how sea horses and hermit crabs are alike and different. Then help them draw each animal.

Living Together

Objective: Children will learn how plants and animals live together.

Get Started

- Ask: **What animals have you seen in a park?**

- Have children describe what the animals were doing and what they might eat. Ask: **How does the park help the animals live?** (The park provides food and shelter.)

Read a Picture

- Show children the pictures on Flipbook page 17.

- Point to each picture and ask children to describe what they see. Ask: **What animals do you see? Where are the animals?**

- Help children see that each environment is different and how it helps the animals that live there.

Flipbook

UNIT C • LESSON 7

Animals live in many places

 Science Facts

Polar bears in the Arctic do not hibernate in winter like other bears do. However, when they have babies, they dig a den in the snow to keep the babies safe and warm.

Related elephant families greet each other when they meet at watering holes. A young elephant learns, at the watering hole, how to suck water into its trunk and then pour it into its mouth. Elephants drink 30 to 50 gallons of water each day.

The other animals pictured are the pronghorn antelope and the three-toed sloth.

17

- Ask children if they see labels on Flipbook page 17. (No)

- Help children label each picture. Write the suggestions on self-stick notes and have volunteers place them on the appropriate picture.

 Informal Assessment

Have groups of children describe the pictures on Flipbook page 17. Observe whether children can name the animals and describe the environment it is in. To help children communicate their ideas, rephrase incomplete sentences as they speak.

Take a Trip

Visit a local zoo and have children name animals they recognize. Encourage them to take notice of each animal's environment or surroundings. When you return to the classroom, have each child tell about something they learned about the animals and where they lived. For example, the polar bears lived by water.

More to Read

Make Way for Ducklings, by Robert McCloskey (Viking, 1976)

A classic story of a mother duck looking for a safe place for her babies.

Activity After reading the book, write the names of all the ducklings in a list. Ask children what they notice about the names. (They all end in -*ack*). Help children play with the ending sound by making up other names for the ducklings. (back, dack, gack, etc.)

Observe and Assess

Use the Flipbook

Revisit the unit's Flipbook pages and discuss them with small groups of children. Assess the children's ability to express their ideas and understanding of the material. Ask them to name some animals and describe parts of a bird and insect.

Use the Big Science Reader

Reread Read *Animals* in the Big Science Reader, Vol. 1 with small groups. As you read, have children identify animals, pointing out similarities and differences. Encourage children to share what they have learned about animals.

Performance Assessment

If children are not yet able to identify insects, birds, and water animals, then give them multiple opportunities to practice identifying them with the Photo Sorting Cards as well as classroom books. You can also provide children with various toy animals to practice identifying different animals.

Additional Activities

Go Further

More About Snails

Science Inquiry Skills: observe, draw a conclusion, communicate

1 Help children list what they have learned about snails or another animals from having them in the classroom.

2 Then ask what questions they still have. List their questions on chart paper.

3 Over the course of two or three days, read books about snails or another classroom animal.

4 Return to the list of questions. After reading books, ask: **Have you learned any answers to your questions?** Record any ideas or answers children have.

 Snails

1. Have one foot
2. Can climb up the side of tank
3. Leave a trail of slime behind them as they move
4. Eat plants and vegetables
5. Can live on water and land

School-to-Home

Be sure to send home the Home Letter from p. R6 with a list of books that children can share with their families.

Life Science UNIT C • Animals

Dear Parents,

We are finishing up our unit in science about animals. We have looked at what animals need to survive and what happens as they grow. We have talked about different types of animals, such as insects, birds, and water animals, and have observed animals in their environment.

Here is a list of books that you can find at your local public library. You can read these books with your child to help reinforce what we are learning in class.

Polar Bear, Polar Bear, What Do You Hear?
by Bill Martin Jr./Eric Carle
(Henry Holt, 1991)

From Egg to Robin
by Susan Canizares
(Scholastic, 1998)

Are You a Grasshopper?
by Judy Allen and Tudor Humphries
(Kingfisher, 2002)

LOG ON **www.macmillanmh.com** for more science online.

Teacher's Notes

Unit Planner

Our Earth

Lesson	Objective	Resources
1 Under Your Feet pp. 80–81	Children will learn about Earth's different surfaces such as rocks, sand, soil, asphalt, cement, and grass.	Flipbook, p. 18
2 Rocks pp. 82–83	Children will learn to describe and sort a variety of rocks based on their properties.	Flipbook, p. 19
3 Land Around Us pp. 84–85	Children will learn about and compare different landforms.	Flipbook, p. 20
4 Water pp. 86–87	Children will learn about different bodies of water, such as oceans, lakes, and streams.	Flipbook, p. 21

Unit Components

Flipbook

Use pages 18–21 to help children learn about the different types of landforms and surfaces, bodies of water and rocks found on our Earth.

Big Science Reader

For Unit D, the story, *What's Under Your Feet?*, exposes children to the different surfaces you can find on Earth. It allows children to explore the various attributes of these surfaces and see familiar surfaces in unfamiliar ways.

Science Songs (CD and Posters)

You can use the songs *What's Under Your Feet?* (tracks 13–14) and *The Ocean Song* (tracks 13–14) for an exciting way to learn about our Earth. Use the posters and have children sing along as they discover what is under their feet as well as what we can do in the ocean.

Materials

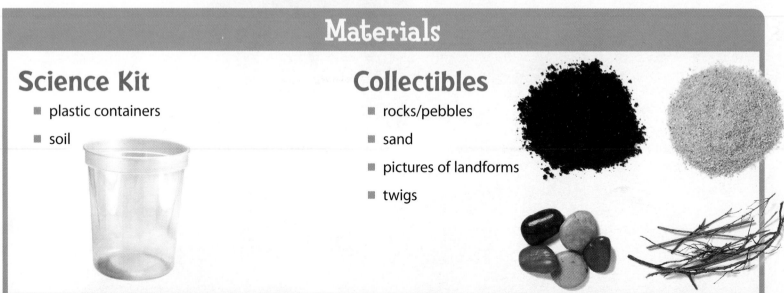

Science Kit
- plastic containers
- soil

Collectibles
- rocks/pebbles
- sand
- pictures of landforms
- twigs

Unit Bibliography

A Gift from the Sea, by Kate Banks (Frances Foster Books, 2001)

A boy finds an ancient rock at the seashore to add to his collection of sea glass and starfish that he has collected at the shore.

Dear Mr. Blueberry, by James Simon (Simon & Schuster, 1991)

A delightful story of a young girl's desire to learn the "truth" about a whale she thinks lives in a pond just outside her home, but whose magical, imaginative understanding of the world around her makes it hard to take in "just the facts!"

Dirt (Jump Into Science), by Steve Tomecek, Nancy Woodman (National Geographic Children's, 2002)

This book explains what soil is made of, how it is formed, and the distinctions among different kinds of soil. It highlights the importance of dirt as a natural resource and its essential role in the lives of animals, plants, and humans.

Rocks: Hard, Soft, Smooth and Rough, by Natalie Rosinsky (Picture Window Books, 2002)

This book discusses three different types of rocks and how they form and change over time. It helps children learn how to classify rocks and provides some simple activities children can do.

The Little House, by Virginia Lee Burton (Houghton Mifflin, 1978)

A city gradually builds up around a little house. When the city completely encircles the house, a family decides its time to take the little house back to the country. The reader watches the landscape change as the house is moved back to the country.

The Seashore Book, by Charlotte Zolotow (HarperCollins, 1992)

A young boy who lives in the mountains learns about the seashore as he and his Mom take an imaginary trip to the shore. The beautifully rendered illustrations help the reader see what it is like at the ocean.

We're Going on a Bear Hunt, by Michael Rosen (Simon & Schuster, 1989)

An illustrated version of the classic children's narrative poem in which a family goes up and down hills, through a river, along the ocean's shore, through a forest, in and out of storms, and caves on their hunt for a bear.

School-to-Home

Be sure to send home the Home Letter from p. R7 with an activity that your students can do with their families.

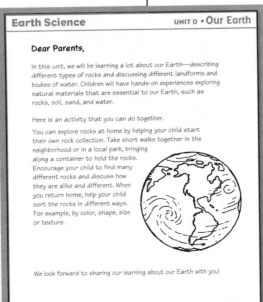

Earth Science　　　　UNIT D • Our Earth

Dear Parents,

In this unit, we will be learning a lot about our Earth—describing different types of rocks and discussing different landforms and bodies of water. Children will have hands-on experiences exploring natural materials that are essential to our Earth, such as rocks, soil, sand, and water.

Here is an activity that you can do together.

You can explore rocks at home by helping your child start their own rock collection. Take short walks together in the neighborhood or in a local park, bringing along a container to hold the rocks. Encourage your child to find many different rocks and discuss how they are alike and different. When you return home, help your child sort the rocks in different ways. For example, by color, shape, size or texture.

We look forward to sharing our learning about our Earth with you!

Bank Street

For more information on these or other books, visit **www.bankstreetbooks.com** or your local library.

Big Science Reader

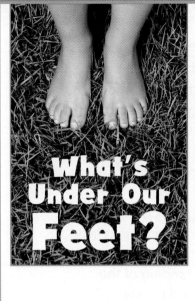

What's Under Our Feet?

Can you guess what this is?

1

Before Reading

- Ask children to name the different types of surfaces they walk on. (sidewalk, beach, woods; Accept all answers.)

- Show children the table of contents and model looking for the page number of the non-fiction selection, *What's Under Our Feet?*

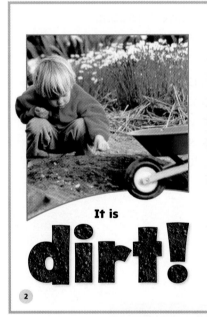

It is **dirt!**

2

Can you guess what this is?

3

During Reading

- As you read the selection, ask children to describe what they see. As they guess what it might be, encourage them to explain their reasoning. For example, *It is dirt because it is brown.*

- On page 4, have children describe the place where the children are. Ask: **What are some other places where you might find sand?** Discuss page 6 in the same way.

It is **sand!**

4

Can you guess what this is?

5

It is a

rock!

6

Can you guess what this is?

7

It is our planet

Earth!

8

- Make two columns on a sheet of chart paper.

- Ask children to think of words that describe what the ground looks like (its color, for example), and write these in the left column.

- In the right column write words that describe what the ground might feel like (for example, squishy, hard, rough).

Teacher Tip

Young children enjoy and learn from telling others about their own experiences. As you discuss the concepts in this chapter, help children make connections between the topics being discussed and experiences they may have had. For example, if you are talking about sand, ask children to share a time when they went to a beach.

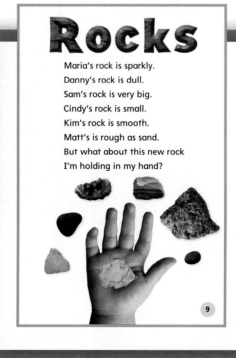

Rocks

Maria's rock is sparkly.
Danny's rock is dull.
Sam's rock is very big.
Cindy's rock is small.
Kim's rock is smooth.
Matt's is rough as sand.
But what about this new rock
I'm holding in my hand?

9

Read the poem *Rocks* on page 9 in the Big Science Reader, Vol. 2. Reread the poem, encouraging children to chime in on the parts they remember.

See pages 31–32 for more reading strategies.

Reread throughout this unit.

Be a Scientist

30 MINUTES SMALL GROUP **Investigation**

Mini Landforms

Objective: Explore landscapes using natural materials.

Science Inquiry Skills: make a model, communicate

1 Discuss with groups of children what kind of landforms they would like to make. Ask: **Will it be hilly? Flat? Will it be made of trees and soil, or rocks and sand?** Display pictures of various landscapes in the Science Center for children to refer to.

2 **Make a Model** Help each group use the materials to create their landforms on large sheets of paper. After they have made the landforms, encourage them to add details using other natural materials. Ask questions such as: **Will there be rocks or trees on your mountain? Besides sand, what else will be on your beach?** Help children decide what materials they might use to add details.

3 **Communicate** Allow each group to share their landforms. Ask children to describe what they made. Encourage the class to ask questions or talk about what they notice.

Materials

- sand
- pebbles and rocks
- soil
- twigs
- leaves
- shells
- pictures of landforms
- large sheets of paper

centers

Math

Rock Groups

Objective: Sort rocks into groups.

Science Inquiry Skills: classify, compare

Materials
- rocks of various shapes, colors, and textures
- two containers

- Have groups of children explore the various rocks. Ask children to describe what they see and feel.
- Ask children to sort the rocks into two different groups; *big* and *small*. Then help children think of their own sorting rule.
- Each time children sort the rocks, have them count how many are in each group. Model using relative terms and descriptors.

Art

Making Mountains

Objective: Make models of different landforms.

Science Inquiry Skills: make a model, observe

Materials
- softened modeling clay

- Show children the modeling clay, and have them explore the various ways they can shape it with their hands.
- Encourage children to make mountains or lakes. Ask questions to help them plan their ideas: **What will the shape of the peak be like? Will there be any rivers flowing down the mountain? What will you make alongside the lake?**

Games

Pairs of Rocks

Objective: Find pairs of cards with matching rocks.

Science Inquiry Skills: compare

Materials
- Photo Sorting Cards #41–50

- Spread the cards face up on a table. Help children describe the characteristics of each rock.
- Now place the cards face down in four rows. Play a concentration game where children take turns turning over two cards, looking for matches.
- After all the matches have been found, have children count how many pairs they each have.

magnetite

magnetite

turquoise

turquoise

Movement

As Tall As a Mountain

Objective: Move and shape your body like different kinds of water, rocks, and mountains.

Science Inquiry Skills: observe, communicate

Materials
- small bell or drum

- Ask children to show how they can move or shape their bodies like a mountain, hill, rock, or body of water. For mountains or hills, have children work with a partner to form that shape.
- Explain that when you ring the bell (or hit the drum) they are to stop moving and listen for directions. Continue with directions such as: *move like a big, tall wave, move like water flowing in a stream, become a tiny pebble, become a large rock.*

Science Activities

Circle Time

WHOLE CLASS

Materials
- three rocks that are different from each other in terms of size, shape, and texture
- small bag
- chart paper

Feel the Difference

Objective: Use sense of touch to identify different types of rocks.

Science Inquiry Skills: observe, communicate, infer

- Explain to children that you are going to pass three different rocks around the circle. Ask them to notice what the rocks feel like in their hands.

- After passing each rock around, have children tell you all the words they can think of to describe what it feels like (for example, smooth, small, heavy, sharp). Give each rock a number (1, 2, or 3) and write the corresponding descriptive words on chart paper.

- After children have had a chance to feel and describe each rock, place one of them in a bag, and put the other two out of sight. Ask for volunteers to come up and guess which rock it is (1, 2, or 3), using only their sense of touch. You may need to remind them of the words they used to describe each rock as they are feeling it. Repeat with the other two rocks.

Singing Time

Sing *What's Under Your Feet?* and *The Ocean Song* throughout this unit.

As children sing along with the CD, point to the text on the poster to help them begin to recognize the link between the words on the page and the words they hear.

Materials
- soil
- sand
- hand lenses
- paper plates

Soil and Sand

Objective: Explore how soil and sand are alike and different.

Science Inquiry Skills: observe, communicate, compare

- Have each child place a handful of soil and a handful of sand on separate plates. Have children describe the sand and the soil. Then give them hand lenses to look at each closely and ask them to describe what they see.

- Draw a Venn diagram on chart paper, and ask children to describe what is alike and different about sand and soil. Record their responses.

Soil   **Sand**

dark brown
soft
squishy
clumpy

made of tiny parts
we walk on it

light color
pours
dry
shiny

Materials
- water table
- two plastic containers
- plastic tubes
- funnels
- water wheel

From Here to There

Objective: Explore how water flows from one place to another.

Science Inquiry Skills: observe, predict, communicate

- Add tubes, funnels and a water wheel to the water (or sand) table. Give children a chance to explore with them to learn how they work.

- Give children two containers. Have them fill one with water (or sand) and leave the other empty. **How can you move the water (sand) from one container to the other without pouring it directly from the full container to the empty one?**

- Repeat, using the water wheel and a container of water. **How can you make the wheel move without pouring the water (sand) directly onto the wheel?**

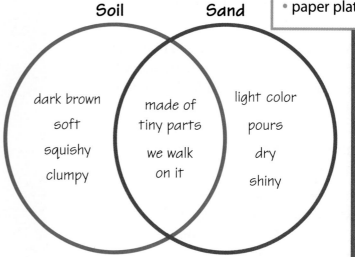

Under Your Feet

Objective: Children will learn about Earth's different surfaces such as rocks, sand, soil, asphalt, cement, and grass.

Get Started

- Ask children to think about a place where the ground outside feels hard under their feet. **Where would you find ground like this?** (Possible Answers: on a sidewalk, in a playground) **What do you think hard ground might be made of?** (Possible Answers: concrete, stone)

- Now ask children to think about a place where the ground outside feels soft under their feet. Repeat the same type of questions as above.

- Have children discuss the activities that you can do on different kinds of ground. For example, you can bounce a ball on hard ground, build a sandcastle in the soft sand, plant something in soil.

Read a Picture

- Show children Flipbook page 18. Ask: **What are the children in this picture doing? What else do you see?**

- Have children describe the different kinds of ground that they see in the picture. Write their responses on separate self-stick notes.

- Read each word, and ask a volunteer to come up and place the self-stick note on that item in the picture.

Flipbook

UNIT D • LESSON 1

What is under their feet?

Science Facts

Boulders were carried by glaciers (ice sheets). The ice ripped away pieces of the solid rock under the soil. When the ice melted, chunks of that rock were left as boulders.

Sand is made of pieces of broken rock. Sand can be white, black, pink or tan, depending on the type of rock it is made from.

Concrete is a mixture of cement, pebbles or sand, and water. It is used in buildings, bridges, and other structures.

Grass grows in lawns, fields and pastures. Wheat, rye, oats, corn, sugarcane, rice and bamboo are kinds of grasses.

Reading in Science

- Model pronoun usage by pointing to the boy in the sand and asking: **What is under *his* feet?**

- Point to the girl, and ask: **What is under *her* feet?**

- Finally, point to each picture and each time ask: **What is under *their* feet?**

✔ Informal Assessment

As children discuss Flipbook page 18 encourage them to use descriptive words to describe the different surfaces. Help children having difficulty by modeling descriptions of the surfaces shown.

18

Teacher Tip

Some of the places in this unit, such as mountains or the ocean, may not be a part of your children's environment. Collect a variety of photographs and related books so that children who have never seen these places can grow more familiar with them.

More to Read

Dirt (Jump Into Science), by Steve Tomecek, Nancy Woodman (National Geographic Children's, 2002)

This book highlights the importance of dirt as a natural resource and its essential role in the lives of animals, plants, and humans.

Activity Create a Venn diagram labeled *Animals* and *Plants.* Have children use the information from the book, as well as what they learned in Units B and C, to describe how soil is important to animals and plants.

Rocks

Objective: Children will learn to describe and sort a variety of rocks based on their properties.

Get Started

- Select two rocks that are different from each other in terms of color, shape, size, and texture.

- Show children the two rocks and ask them to describe the differences they notice between them. Help them to think about all the ways they could be different. Ask: **What is different about their size? Their shape? How they feel?** Record their responses.

Read a Picture

- Display Flipbook page 19 and have children help you count how many rocks are on the page. Read the statement at the top of the page, and ask children to describe what they notice about each rock.

- As children discuss the different rocks, encourage them to use position words (such as above, below, next to, between) to indicate which rocks they are referring to.

- Help children generate a list of descriptive words to describe each rock.

Describe these rocks.

Science Facts

Pyrite is commonly known as "Fool's Gold."

River rocks become smooth in rushing water.

Sandstone contains grains of sand held together.

Quartz is a clear, hard rock that is the main ingredient in sand.

Orbicular rhyolite is a mineral, a substance found in nature that is not alive. Salt, coal and gold are minerals.

Metamorphic Gneiss has been exposed to a lot of pressure and heat. Gneiss is used to pave roads and make buildings.

Granite is so hard that it is used to build statues and buildings.

19

- Reread the statement and ask children to listen for the beginning sound in the word *rocks*.

- Ask children: **What other words begin with same sound as *rocks*?** Record their responses.

✓ Informal Assessment

Observe children as they sort and describe the rocks on the Flipbook page. Some children may need to sort rocks one attribute at a time. Provide these children with additional sorting opportunities.

Take a Trip

Plan a trip outside to go on a rock hunt. Before going out to collect rocks, ask children to predict what kinds of rocks they may find. Record their predictions on chart paper. As you walk around the school yard or neighborhood, encourage children to try to find five rocks that are different from each other. When you return to the classroom, have them sort the rocks in small groups. Invite children to tell a partner about the rocks they found. Revisit with children the predictions they made earlier and check to see if any of their predictions were correct.

More to Read

Rocks: Hard, Soft, Smooth and Rough, by Natalie Rosinsky (Picture Window Books, 2002)

This book discusses three different types of rocks and how they form and change over time. It helps children learn how to classify rocks and provides some simple activities children can do.

Activity After reading this book, select a few of the rocks you and the children have collected and help children try to classify them according to the categories discussed in the book.

Land Around Us

Objective: Children will learn about and compare different landforms.

Get Started

- Ask children if they have ever seen a mountain or hill. Ask: **What kinds of activities do you think you can do on a hill or a mountain? Do you think you can ride a bike? Why or why not?**

Read a Picture

- Display Flipbook page 20. Read the question and have children describe how the two pictures are alike and different.

- Ask: **Why do you think there are no plants on the mountain in this picture? Do you think people could live at the top of this mountain? Why or why not? Do you think people live near this hill? Why or why not?**

- Remind children of your earlier discussions of rocks and soil. Have them look carefully at the two pictures and tell you what they think the hills and mountains might be made of. Ask them to explain their thinking.

- Explain that a hill can never be as high as a mountain.

What do you see?

 ## Science Facts

A **mountain** is a mass of land that rises at least 3,000 feet above the surrounding area. Some mountains are so high that the atmosphere at the peaks is freezing, and any precipitation comes down as snow. The Himalayas, in Nepal and Tibet, are the tallest mountains in the world. In California, the tallest mountain is Mount Whitney.

A **hill** is a raised, rounded part of the earth's surface. A hill rises no higher than 3,000 feet, shorter than a mountain. The low land between hills is called a valley.

20

- Have children listen for the last sound in the words *mountains* and *hills*.

- Ask: **What do you notice about those words?** (they both end with the *s* sound) Ask children to think of other words that end in the same sound. Record their responses.

- Explain that often the letter *s* at the end of a word makes it plural, meaning there is more than one.

 **Informal Assessment**

Ask children to describe the differences between a mountain and a hill. If children are having difficulty, help them to see that size is a clear difference between the two landforms.

 EL

Collect a variety of objects that illustrate comparisons such as taller/shorter, bigger/smaller, wider/narrower. Have children choose two objects from one category. Model using comparative language to describe the objects and have children repeat after you. For more advanced EL students, model using full sentences to describe the objects:

The _____ is taller (shorter) than the _____ .

 More to Read

Going on a Bear Hunt, by Michael Rosen (Simon & Schuster, 1989)

This book follows the adventures of a family that decided to go on a bear hunt. When they found what they were looking for, they beat a hasty retreat, back through all the landforms they traversed on their hunt.

Activity Review the book and have children help you make a list of all the different places the family traveled. Allow children to draw each place and make into a class book.

Water

Objective: Children will learn about different bodies of waters, such as oceans, lakes, and streams.

Get Started

- Ask children to talk about a time when they were at an outside place with water. Encourage them to tell about the body of water in as much detail as possible. As they talk, ask if they know the name of this place. For example: **Was it the ocean, a pond, stream, or pool?**

- Have children tell you what they know about water. Ask: **Where can we find water outside? Why is water important? What different kinds of water are there?**

Read a Picture

- Show children page 21 of the Flipbook. Have them describe what they see in each picture, encouraging them to use full sentences.

- Read the question and invite volunteers to point to the water in each picture. Then encourage them to discuss the movement of the water in each picture. Explain that the pictures show a stream, lake, and an ocean.

- Have children discuss different activities you can or cannot do in each body of water such as swimming , boating, and fishing.

Where is the water?

 ## Science Facts

Streams carry rain and melting snow from the mountains to rivers and lakes, and finally to the ocean. As the water from a stream falls over the rocks, it smoothes the rocks' rough edges.

A **lake** is a body of water surrounded by land. Lake water is usually fresh, not salty. Because the water in a lake is not wavy, lakes are often good for swimming. Lakes are larger than ponds.

The **ocean** is the whole body of salt water that covers three-fourths of the earth's surface. Gravity from the Sun and Moon pull the ocean's waters, causing tides. Large waves start out at sea and slowly wash toward beaches.

21

- Help children remember what a label is.

- Encourage children to think of labels for each picture.

- Write labels on self-stick notes and have volunteers place them on the correct pictures.

✔ Informal Assessment

Some children may have difficulty with the differences between streams, lakes, and oceans. Share simple maps that illustrate the different shapes and sizes of various bodies of water.

Finger Play

I found a great big shell one day (cup hands)
Upon the ocean floor.
I held it close up to my ear (raise hands to ear)
I heard the ocean roar!
I found a tiny shell one day (cup one hand)
Upon the ocean sand.
The waves had worn it nice and smooth
It felt nice in my hand.

More to Read

The Seashore Book, by Charlotte Zolotow
(HarperCollins, 1992)

A young boy who lives in the mountains learns about the seashore as he and his Mom take an imaginary trip to the shore. The beautifully rendered illustrations help the reader "see" what it is like at the ocean.

Activity   After reading this book about the shore, hide seashells and small pebbles in the sand table for children to find. Encourage children to describe what they need.

Observe and Assess

Use the Flipbook

Revisit the unit's Flipbook pages and discuss them with small groups of children. Assess children's ability to express their understanding of different types of ground, rocks, landforms, and bodies of water by asking them to describe the landforms and sort the rocks.

Use the Big Science Reader

Reread *What's Under Our Feet?* in the Big Science Reader, Vol. 2 with small groups. Have children describe the various types of material that the ground is made of, and how these may look different up close and from far away.

Performance Assessment

If children are still not able to describe the differences among various types of rocks, continue to play games with the Photo Sorting Cards to give them more experience with the attributes that differentiate rocks from each other, such as size, color, shape, and texture.

turquoise

marble

river rock

coal

mica

Additional Activities

Go Further

Rain, Rain Everywhere

1 In small groups, have children create another mini-landform like the one they made in the "Be a Scientist" activity or they can use the one they already made.

2 Explain that this time they will make it "rain" on their landscape. Ask them to predict what they think will happen to each part of their landscape when the rain falls on it. If they say that it will wash away, ask them what materials they could add to make it stronger or more solid.

3 After children have changed or added materials to their landscape to make it rain-resistant, have them sprinkle water on it with a watering can. Discuss how it changed, and what helped the materials to stay together.

School-to-Home

Be sure to send home the Home Letter from p. R8 with a list of books that your students can share with their families.

Earth Science　　　　　UNIT D • Our Earth

Dear Parents,

We are finishing up our unit about our Earth. We have looked at various types of ground material, such as rocks, sand, soil, asphalt, cement, and grass. We have explored and sorted different kinds of rocks, and have learned about hills and mountains, oceans, lakes, and streams.

Here are some books that you can find at your local public library. You can read these books with your child to help reinforce what we are learning in class.

Rocks: Hard, Soft, Smooth and Rough
by Natalie Rosinsky
(Picture Window Books, 2002)

Let's Go Rock Collecting (Let's Read and Find Out Science, Stage 2)
by Roma Gans, Holly Keller
(HarperTrophy, 1997)

Dirt (Jump Into Science)
by Steve Tomecek, Nancy Woodman
(National Geographic Children's, 2002)

 www.macmillanmh.com for more science online.

Teacher's Notes

Unit Planner

Sky and Weather

Lesson	Objective	Resources
1 Day and Night pp. 100–101	Children will learn what the day and night sky look like.	Flipbook, p. 22
2 All Kinds of Weather pp. 102–103	Children will learn how different types of weather affect people.	Flipbook, p. 23
3 Weather Changes pp. 104–105	Children will learn how weather can change.	Flipbook, p. 24
4 The Seasons pp. 106–107	Children will learn about the four seasons.	Flipbook, p. 25

Unit Components

Flipbook

Use pages 22–25 to help children learn about the different types of weather and seasons there are. Help them make the connection between weather, what to wear, and choice of activities.

Big Science Reader

For Unit E, the story, *What Might You Wear?*, exposes children to the different types of weather there are and how to prepare for each condition. This story helps children understand how we are affected by weather.

Science Songs (CD and Posters)

You can use the songs *Day Sky and Night Sky* (tracks 17–18) and *The Seasons* (tracks 19–20) for an exciting way to learn about weather. Children can use these songs to help them think about what they can do in each season. Use the posters and have children sing along as they discover different weather and seasons.

Materials

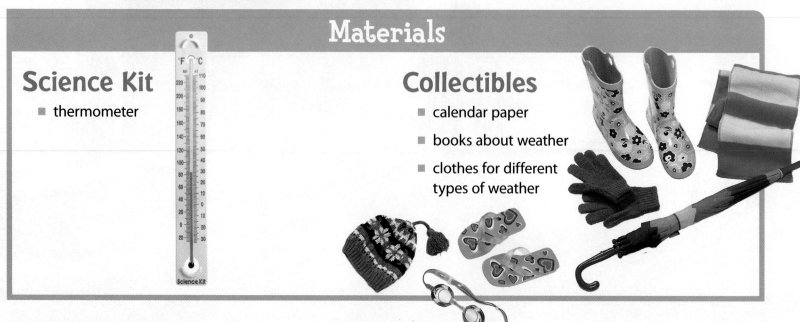

Science Kit
- thermometer

Collectibles
- calendar paper
- books about weather
- clothes for different types of weather

Unit Bibliography

Days in Fall, by Vic Parker
(Raintree, 2005)

Days in Spring, by Vic Parker
(Raintree, 2005)

Each of these books uses color photographs and simple text to show how each season is different.

Days in Summer, by Vic Parker
(Raintree, 2005)

Days in Winter, by Vic Parker
(Raintree, 2005)

Night and Day, by Alvin Granowski
(Millbrook Press, Inc. 2001)

This book describes events that happen during the day and at night, both inside children's homes and outside in the natural world.

Watching the Weather, by Miranda Ashwell and Andy Owen (Heinemann Library, 1999)
Use this book to explain how weather forecasters predict the weather.

Wind, by Miranda Ashwell and Andy Owen (Heinemann Library, 1999)

Children will enjoy learning facts about wind and seeing colorful photographs in this book.

School-to-Home

Be sure to send home the Home Letter from p. R9 with an activity that your students can do with their families.

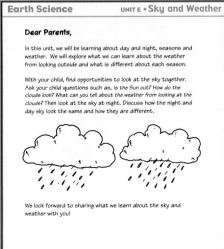

Earth Science   UNIT E • Sky and Weather

Dear Parents,

In this unit, we will be learning about day and night, seasons and weather. We will explore what we can learn about the weather from looking outside and what is different about each season.

With your child, find opportunities to look at the sky together. Ask your child questions such as, *Is the Sun out? How do the clouds look? What can you tell about the weather from looking at the clouds?* Then look at the sky at night. Discuss how the night and day sky look the same and how they are different.

We look forward to sharing what we learn about the sky and weather with you!

Bank Street

For more information on these or other books, visit **www.bankstreetbooks.com** or your local library.

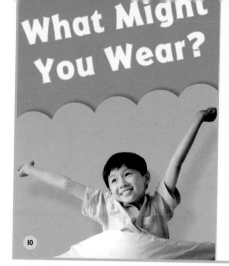

What might you wear on a hot summer day?

10

11

A bathing suit!

12

What might you wear on a cool fall day?

13

A sweater!

14

What might you wear on a cold winter day?

15

Before Reading

- Tell children you want them to help you make two lists. Ask: **What do you wear when it is hot outside?** Record their responses.

- Ask: **What do you wear when it is cold outside?** Record children's responses.

- Model using the table of contents, to find the page number for the story, *What Might You Wear?*

During Reading

- As you read, give children time to discuss what they might wear on each kind of day.

- Encourage children to give reasons for their clothing choices, for example, wearing a hat to keep your head warm in cold weather.

A coat!

16

What might you wear
on a warm spring day?

17

Gardening gloves!

18

Weather

"What shall I wear today?"
I asked my mom.
She said, "Look outside,
Are there clouds or just Sun?"

So I looked out the window,
And what did I see?
I saw clouds that's for sure,
And rain falling on trees.

So I dressed for the rain,
And I'm glad that I looked.
I picked up my umbrella.
It's the last thing I took.

19

After Reading

■ Go back to the list of clothes for hot and cold weather. Reread each list.

■ Ask children if they want to add more clothing to the lists. Record their responses.

Read the poem *Weather* on p. 19 in the Big Science Reader, Vol. 2 .

Reread the poem, inviting children to join in on parts they remember.

Read this poem throughout the unit.

See pages 31–32 for more reading strategies.

Science Activities

Be a Scientist

 15 MINUTES   **WHOLE CLASS** **Investigation**

Weather Calendar

Materials

- large construction paper
- markers

Objective: Make a calendar to keep track of weather over the year.

Science Inquiry Skills: observe, communicate, predict

1 **Observe** Discuss with children what weather is.
Ask: **Does weather change?** (yes) **How do you know?**
What are some different kinds of weather that we see or feel? (hot, cold, wet, dry, rainy, snowy, etc.)

2 **Communicate** Explain that in order to learn how the weather changes, you are going to work together to record information about the weather.

3 Show children your calendar, and explain that each day a child will draw a picture showing the type of weather outside.

4 Talk with children about the different weather words they can use to help describe the weather each day. Generate a list of possible weather symbols children can draw (a Sun, cloud, Sun and cloud together, cloud with rain). Model how you will write the weather words each day beneath the picture.

5 Begin your calendar with that day's weather.

6 **Predict** Each day invite children to make predictions about what the weather might be like the next day.

centers

Dramatic Play

Is it Cold?

Objective: Act out different kinds of weather.

Science Inquiry Skills: communicate, observe

- During Circle Time, ask: **What do you do when it is cold and snowy outside?** List children's responses. Repeat the process with hot and sunny weather.

- Discuss different ways to act out weather activities. Display pictures of different weather scenes and provide appropriate dress-up clothes such as gloves and a hat for children to use during Center Time.

Materials
- clothes for various types of weather
- pictures of different weather scenes

Games

Night or Day?

Objective: Recognize things that we see at day and night.

Science Inquiry Skills: observe, classify

- Place the Photo Sorting Cards in several rows facedown. Have children take turns turning the cards over and identifying the pictures.

- Then place the cards in a pile facedown. Children take turns taking the top card and sorting it into one of two categories: *things you see at night and things you see in the day.* Have children place the cards for night on a sheet of dark-colored paper, and the card for day, on a piece of light-colored paper.

Materials
- Photo Sorting Cards #51–60
- construction paper

crescent Moon

clouds

Art

Paint the Night Sky

Objective: Learn about the night sky.

Science Inquiry Skills: communicate, make a model

- Ask children to describe what they might see in the night sky.

- Invite children to paint the sky on dark construction paper. Encourage them to think about making patterns in the sky.

Materials
- dark blue or black construction paper
- white and yellow paint
- paintbrushes

Diego

Library

Book Look

Objective: Explore weather through books.

Science Inquiry Skills: observe

- Collect books about different kinds of weather and place them in your classroom library.

- At Circle Time, show children the books and tell them they will be in the Library Center.

- Encourage children to look at the books on their own or with a partner.

Materials
- books about weather

Science Activities

Circle Time

WHOLE CLASS

Materials
- two-column chart labeled *Hot* and *Cold*
- self-stick notes with each child's name
- chart paper

Favorite Kinds of Weather

Objective: Children talk about what kind of weather they like and why.

Science Inquiry Skills: compare, classify

- Invite each child to say whether they like hot weather or cold weather. Have children come up and put a self-stick note with their name on it in one of the two columns on the chart.

- Work with children to count how many children like hot weather and how many like cold weather. Record the results.

- Ask: **Do more children like hot weather or cold weather?**

- Repeat on other days with different categories, for example, rainy/snowy, windy/not windy, cloudy/sunny.

Hot Weather	Cold Weather
Dylan	
Lucy	
	Rusty
Rasha	

Singing Time

Sing *Day Sky and Night Sky* and *The Seasons* with your class throughout this unit. Show children the words to the song on the corresponding Song Poster. Invite children to sing as you point to the words on the poster. Repeat throughout this unit.

Move Like the Wind

Objective: Use gross motor skills to communicate to others.

Science Inquiry Skills: communicate

- Tell children they are going to move like different kinds of weather. Have each group try one of the following weather situations and act it out for the rest of the children in the group. Encourage the other children to guess the weather. You might want to play appropriate music, such as a weather sounds CD, to inspire children.

  - heavy rainstorm

  - snow falling gently

  - extreme wind

  - gentle breeze

Materials
- small paper bags

A Season Walk

Objective: Learn how the seasons affect your immediate surroundings.

Science Inquiry Skills: observe, communicate

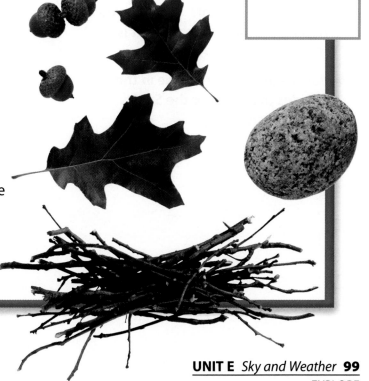

- Take children out to the playground, a local park, or for a walk in the neighborhood.

- Have children observe the following: air, people, animals, trees, and plants. Give each small group a bag to collect nature items they find.

- When you return to the classroom, have children share what they found and discuss what they observed. Repeat this activity in different types of weather.

Day and Night

Objective: Children will learn what the day and night sky look like.

Get Started

- Ask: **How do you know when it is night time? What do you see in the sky at night? How do you know when it is daytime? What do you see in the sky during the day?**

Read a Picture

- Cover the night sky photo on Flipbook page 22. Show children the day sky. Have children describe what they see.

- Then uncover the night sky. Have children describe what they see.

- Ask: **What is different about the sky at night and during the day? What is similar?**

- Ask: **What do you think happens to the Sun when it is night? What do you think happens to the Moon when it is day?** (Accept all responses.)

- Ask: **What else can we see in the sky besides the Moon or the Sun?** (clouds, stars)

What can we see in the sky?

day

 Science Facts

When the sky looks dark, it is because our side of Earth is facing away from the Sun. The light areas on the Moon are higher areas called *terrae*. The dark areas on the Moon are cratered areas called *maria*.

The sky looks light during the day because our part of Earth is facing the Sun. In the sky, we can see clouds made of tiny water droplets or ice crystals. Most clouds change shape constantly, as new droplets form in some parts of the cloud and evaporate in other parts. The wind also pushes clouds and makes them change shape.

night

22

- After discussing the images on the page, reread the question, *What can we see in the sky?*

- Have children help you count the number of words in the question. (7)

- Write the words *we* and *see* on the board. Read them aloud. Ask children what they notice about these two words. (They rhyme.)

- Have them help you think of other words that rhyme. (me, tree, bee, he, knee, tea, we) Write the words that rhyme on the board.

✓ Informal Assessment

If you notice that some children are unclear about how the night and day skies are different, encourage children to look at the night sky when they are home and tell them that they can describe what they see the next day at Circle Time.

Teacher Tip

Children will have a difficult time understanding why they only see the Moon and stars at night. Keep reinforcing the idea that the Moon and stars are always in the sky even when they cannot see them.

Explain how the bright light from the Sun often blocks out the light from stars and the Moon during the day.

More to Read

Night and Day, by Alvin Granowski
(Millbrook Press, Inc. 2001)
Read this book to discuss more about night and day.

Activity Discuss with children what happens in the day and what happens at night. Then help them make a day sky and a night sky using black and white construction paper, cotton balls for clouds, white paper for stars, and yellow for the Sun.

All Kinds of Weather

Objective: Children will learn how different types of weather affect people.

Get Started

- Invite children to look at the weather calendar you started in the *Be a Scientist* activity. If you have had any rainy days, point them out.

- Ask: **What do you do when you have to go outside in the rain?**

Read a Picture

- Display Flipbook page 23. Read the question. As children make their observations, ask: **How do you know?**

- Ask: **What is happening to the ground? Will the ground stay like this? Why or why not?** (No; puddles will dry when the Sun comes out.)

- Ask: **What are the people in this picure wearing and carrying that tells us it is raining?**

- Ask: **How do you think these people feel about the rain? How do you feel about the rain?**

Flipbook

UNIT E • LESSON 2

What can we tell about this weather?

 Science Facts

Rain is part of the water cycle. Water evaporates from the ocean and other bodies of water, goes into the air, and then forms clouds. Eventually, the water particles in the air become heavy and they fall back to Earth. Then the whole process repeats. Rain cleans the air by washing away dust and pollution.

People use umbrellas and raincoats to protect themselves from the rain. When umbrellas were first invented, they protected ancient Egyptians from the Sun. Raincoats were invented in Scotland in 1823. They were originally made of a layer of rubber between two layers of cloth.

Reading in Science

- After discussing the weather, go back and reread the question.

- Remind children that this is a question, so the ending mark is called a question mark.

- Go back to previous pages and help children look for and identify sentences that end with a question mark.

✓ Informal Assessment

If children have not been outside when it is rainy, try to plan a Rainy Day Walk. Ask parents to send their children to school with raincoats and boots, if possible, when it rains. Then take small groups for walks in the schoolyard. Discuss how things look, smell and feel different when it is raining.

Finger Play

The Eensy Weensy Spider
Crawled up the water spout.
Down came the rain and washed the spider out.
Out came the Sun and dried up all the rain,
And the Eensy Weensy Spider
Crawled up the spout again.

More to Read

Wind, by Miranda Ashwell and Andy Owen (Heinemann Library, 1999)

Read this book to learn more about wind.

Activity   Bring in a small fan. Give each child a chance to see what it feels like on his or her face. Have children help you make a class poem. Begin each line of your class poem with the sentence: *Wind is* _____ .

Weather Changes

Objective: Children will learn how weather can change.

Get Started

- Ask children how they decide what to wear before going to school. **How do you know what the weather is like?**

Read a Picture

- Show children page 24 of the Flipbook and read the question. Have children describe how they know that it is a warm, **sunny day.** (children in short sleeved shirts, the Sun is out)

- Next have children talk about how the sky might change if it were about to rain. **How would the children in the picture know? What do you think they might do?**

- Discuss with children which activities are best for warm weather. Ask: **What activities are the people in the picture able to do because it is not raining?**

Flipbook

UNIT E • LESSON 3

What can we tell about this weather?

 Science Facts

The Sun, is a giant star that is billions of miles away. The Sun warms our land, air, and water and gives us light.

Wind is air that is moving over the earth. It happens when air moves from a warmer, high-pressure area to a cooler, low-pressure area.

Shadows happen when light is blocked by an object. Objects that are farther from the ground make fuzzier-looking shadows. Objects that are closer to the ground make sharper-looking shadows. As Earth spins on its axis, shadows change in size and direction.

Reading in Science

- After discussing the picture, reread the question.

- Ask children if it is a sentence or a question and how they know.

- Help children generate their own questions about weather, write each question on chart paper and point out the question marks you write.

✅ Informal Assessment

Encourage children to share their favorite outdoor activities. Have them tell which activities are best for warm, sunny weather and why. If children are having difficulty describing appropriate activities for warm weather, show them pictures of such activities. For example, children playing baseball, jumping rope, riding a bike.

EL

Work with children in a small group, giving them time to discuss what is happening on the Flipbook page. Point to each image in the picture and help children hear and eventually use the words that name or describe characteristics of the images on the page.

More to Read

Watching the Weather, by Miranda Ashwell and Andy Owen (Heinemann Library, 1999)

Read this book to learn more about weather.

Activity   Fold sheets of paper in half to make small blank books. Place in the Writing Center. Encourage children to make books about things to do in warm weather.

The Seasons

Objective: Children will learn about the four seasons.

Get Started

- Ask: **What season is it?** The season we are in now is fall (or winter, etc.). Discuss the weather, activities, and clothing that are common to the season.

Read a Picture

- Open to Flipbook page 25 and read the question.

- Help children find the picture that represents the current season.

- Discuss what typically happens in each season by describing what is in each picture.

- Help children discuss how the seasons where they live are like the pictures, and how they are different.

- Encourage children to notice the different clothes the children are wearing in each picture.

What are the four seasons?

winter   spring

Science Facts

Fall In certain areas of the U.S., leaves change color in the fall. Trees stop making food and the leaves' chlorophyll disappears.

Winter In winter, the northern hemisphere is tilted away from the Sun. We see the Sun for fewer hours each day. Ice crystals fall from clouds and join together to make snow.

Spring During spring, Earth is tilted neither towards nor away from the Sun. For this reason, the weather is more moderate.

Summer In summer, the northern hemisphere is tilted towards the Sun. The Sun appears higher in the sky. We get more intense sunlight, more hours of daylight, and warmer temperatures.

summer

fall

25

Reading in Science

- Remind children what a label is. Read the label below each picture.

- After discussing each image, help children generate a list of possible labels for the photographs.

- Write each label on a self-stick note and place it next to the corresponding picture.

✓ Informal Assessment

Have groups of children talk about what they can do in each season. If children have difficulty understanding the changes that happen with each season, provide images of activities they can do in the different seasons, for example, swimming in the summer.

Teacher Tip

If children live in a climate without marked seasonal changes, then talk about the things that do change. Also, try to read books about what it looks and feels like when seasons change in other parts of the country. Display pictures of the seasons in other areas of the country around the classroom and visit them throughout this unit.

More to Read

Days in Fall, by Vic Parker (Raintree, 2005)
Days in Summer, by Vic Parker (Raintree, 2005)
Days in Winter, by Vic Parker (Raintree, 2005)
Days in Spring, by Vic Parker (Raintree, 2005)

Read these four books about the seasons over the course of four days.

Activity After reading each book, make one class book for each season including things to do and what that season may look like.

Observe and Assess

Use the Flipbook

Revisit the unit's Flipbook pages and discuss them with small groups of children. Have children name the four seasons and describe an activity they can do in each one.

Reread

Read *What Might You Wear?* in the Big Science Reader, Vol. 2 with small groups. As you read, have children identify the different kinds of weather and discuss why people are wearing what they are wearing.

Performance Assessment

To find out more about what children know about weather, have them draw pictures that represent different types of weather. Invite them to tell about their pictures. Compile children's drawings into a class weather book.

Additional Activities

Go Further

Weather Graph

Science Inquiry Skills: communicate

1 Help children use their weather calendar to analyze the information they recorded.

2 Count the number of sunny and rainy days. Create a two-column bar graph to show the information.

3 Discuss the other types of weather recorded on the calendar. Try additional two-column bar graphs such as windy, not windy; cloudy, not cloudy.

School-to-Home

Be sure to send home the Home Letter from p. R10 with a list of books that children can share with their families.

Earth Science UNIT E • Sky and Weather

Dear Parents,

We are finishing up our unit about sky and weather. We have explored what is different about the sky during the day and at night. We have discussed what you can tell about the weather by looking outside and your child has learned about each season.

Here is a list of books that you can find at your local public library. You can read these books with your child to help reinforce what we are learning in class.

Night and Day
by Alvin Granowski
(Millbrook Press, Inc., 2001)

Wind
by Miranda Ashwell and Andy Owen
(Heinemann Library, 1999)

Watching the Weather
by Miranda Ashwell and Andy Owen
(Heinemann Library, 1999)

LOG ON www.macmillanmh.com for more science online.

Teacher's Notes

Matter and Motion

Lesson	Objective	Resources
1 Heat It Up! pp. 120–121	Children will learn how hot water can change spaghetti.	Flipbook, p. 26
2 Freeze It Up! pp. 122–123	Children will learn what happens when a liquid freezes.	Flipbook, p. 27
3 Mix It Up! pp. 124–125	Children will learn how matter can change when mixed together.	Flipbook, p. 28
4 Push and Pull pp. 126–127	Children will learn how objects can be moved by pushing and pulling.	Flipbook, p. 29
5 Magnets pp. 128–129	Children will learn what magnets do and where they can stick.	Flipbook, p. 30

Flipbook

Use pages 26–30 to help children learn about the different ways matter can change and move.

Big Science Reader

For Unit F, the story *Water*, exposes children to the different ways water can move and the forms it can take.

Science Songs (CD and Posters)

You can use the songs *Let's Heat, Mix, and Freeze* (tracks 21-22) and *Push and Pull* (tracks 23-24) for an exciting way to learn about the motion of matter. Use the posters and have children sing along with the CD as they discover how matter changes and the pushing and pulling of objects.

Materials

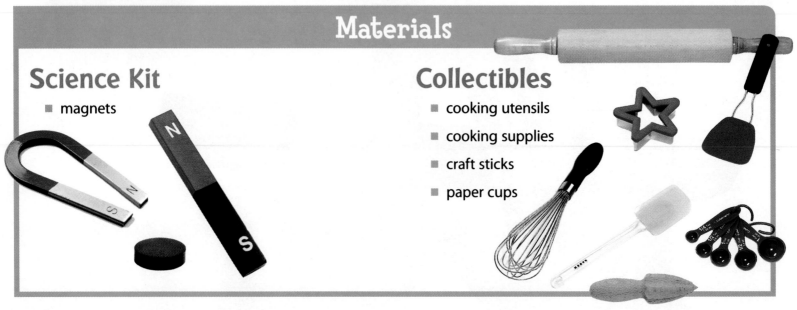

Science Kit

- magnets

Collectibles

- cooking utensils
- cooking supplies
- craft sticks
- paper cups

From Wax to Crayon, by Michael H. Forman (Children's Press, Inc. 1997)

Detailed photographs show each step in the production of crayons.

Magnets, by Angela Royston (Heinemann, 2002)

This book explains what magnets are, how they are used in everyday life, and even shows how to make your own magnet.

Pulling, by Patricia Whitehouse (Heinemann Library, 2003)

Each of these books uses photographs and simple text to explore when and how people move objects through pushing and pulling.

Pushing, by Patricia Whitehouse (Heinemann Library, 2003)

Solids, Liquids, and Gasses, by Angela Royston (Heinemann, 2002)

This book explains how things melt and freeze, as well as other ways matter changes shape.

What's for Lunch? Milk, by Claire Llewellyn (Children's Press, 1998)

Milk goes from the farm to the processing plant, and then gets mixed into special treats like ice cream.

School-to-Home

Be sure to send home the Home Letter from p. R11 with an activity that your students can do with their families.

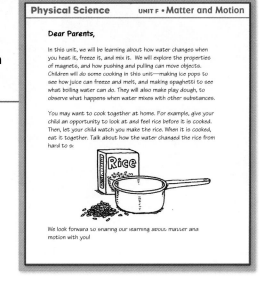

Physical Science UNIT F • Matter and Motion

Dear Parents,

In this unit, we will be learning about how water changes when you heat it, freeze it, and mix it. We will explore the properties of magnets, and how pushing and pulling can move objects. Children will do some cooking in this unit—making ice pops to see how juice can freeze and melt, and making spaghetti to see what boiling water can do. They will also make play dough, to observe what happens when water mixes with other substances.

You may want to cook together at home. For example, give your child an opportunity to look at and feel rice before it is cooked. Then, let your child watch you make the rice. When it is cooked, eat it together. Talk about how the water changed the rice from hard to so

We look forward to sharing our learning about matter and motion with you!

Bank Street

For more information on these or other books, visit **www.bankstreetbooks.com** or your local library.

Bank Street

MACMILLAN McGRAW-HILL
Science

Big Science Reader

Volume 2

Before Reading

- Ask children: **What are some places where you can see water outside?**

- Record their responses.

During Reading

- As you read, stop and discuss children's experiences. Ask: **Where else have you seen frozen water?**

- Discuss how water can move in different ways as well as take on many forms such as ice and rain.

Water ripples over rocks,

20

and splashes down a hill.

21

Water freezes when it is cold,

22

making ice under our feet.

23

Water falls from clouds as rain,

24

and sometimes falls as snow.

25

Sometimes water splashes high,

26

and sometimes doesn't move at all.

27

■ Go back to the list of places where children have seen water outside.

■ Ask children if they want to add to the list. Record their ideas.

This is Water

Tumbling water from waterfalls,
Icy streams and streets.
Water falling from the clouds,
Rain and snow and sleet.

Water moving in and out,
On shores across the beach.
Water staying very still,
Beneath our little feet!

28

29

Read the poem *This is Water* on pages 28-29 of the Big Science Reader, Vol. 2.

Reread the poem, inviting children to join in on parts they remember. See page 32 for more reading strategies.

Reread this poem throughout the unit.

Be a Scientist

 15 MINUTES WHOLE CLASS

Investigation

Freeze It, Melt It, Eat It!

Objective: Explore different forms of juice.

Science Inquiry Skills: observe, predict, communicate

Materials

- grape juice
- plastic wrap
- rubber bands
- paper cups
- craft sticks

1 Ask children to describe the properties of grape juice. (purple, wet, liquid, sweet) Ask: **What will we have to do to make ice pops from this juice?**

2 Have children pour juice into a cup. Make two extra cups to be used in steps 4 and 5. Cover with plastic wrap, secure with a rubber band, and push a craft stick through the plastic wrap.

3 Observe When the pops are frozen, ask: **How did the juice change? What do the pops look like? Feel like? Taste like?** Record children's responses.

4 Predict Ask: **What will happen if we leave one pop in a shady spot and one in a sunny spot? Which will melt more quickly? Why?** Place one pop in a shady spot and another in a sunny spot.

5 Communicate Record how long it took for each ice pop to melt. **Which melted first?** Help children discuss why one melted more quickly. Revisit children's predictions.

centers

Blocks

Materials
- blocks
- toy trucks
- toy cars

Moving Around

Objective: To explore how objects move.

Science Inquiry Skills: investigate

- Throughout this unit, encourage children to explore how to create structures that allow the toy cars and trucks to move.

- As they work, ask: **What did you do to help the car (truck) move?** (push, pull) **What could you build so that cars can move on their own?** (build ramps)

Math

Materials
- plastic pan
- small objects (paper clip, unifix cube, buttons, rubber band, sewing thimble, index card)
- magnets
- chart paper

Graph It!

Objective: To sort and graph objects.

Science Inquiry Skills: classify, communicate

- Prepare a graph for each child that shows each object and has two columns labeled, *Sticks to Magnets; Does Not Stick.*

- Show children a plastic pan filled with a variety of small objects.

- Ask children to sort the objects into two groups: *ones that stick to magnets, ones that do not.*

- Then have children check off the correct column as they test to see which objects stick to the magnets.

Art

Materials
- fingerpaint in primary colors (red, yellow, blue)
- paper

Paint Colors

Objective: To explore mixing colors together.

Science Inquiry Skills: predict, investigate

- Hold up different colors of paint and ask: **What do you think will happen if we combine some of these colors?** (Accept all responses.)

- As children work with the fingerpaints, encourage them to experiment with combining different colors.

Water Table

Materials
- water table
- water wheel

Water Wheel

Objective: To explore how water moves.

Science Inquiry Skills: investigate, communicate

- At Circle Time, show children the wheel and explain that it will be in the Water Table.

- As children work, ask: **How slowly can you make the wheel move? How fast can it move? What did you do to make it move at different speeds?**

Circle Time

WHOLE CLASS

Pop the Popcorn

Objective: Learn that heat can change matter and observe motion.

Science Inquiry Skills: communicate, observe

Materials
- sheet
- foam ball
- popcorn kernels (unpopped)
- popcorn

- Show children some uncooked popcorn. Have children describe its properties. (hard, small, yellow)

- Show some popped corn and ask: **How has the popcorn changed?** (bigger, softer, white) **What do you think made it change?** (heat)

- Tell children they are going to pretend the foam ball is a popcorn kernel and they are going to bounce it on the sheet to "pop" it.

- Have each child hold the edge of the sheet. Place the foam ball in the middle. Encourage children to try to keep the ball in the air by moving the sheet up and down. Discuss how kernels are moved around through hot air in order for them to pop.

Singing Time

Sing *Let's Heat, Mix, and Freeze* and *Push and Pull* with your class throughout this unit. Allow children to sing along with the CD as they use the pictures and words on the posters to make a link between what they hear and see.

Small Group

Mix Play Dough

Materials
- water
- bowl
- spoon
- measuring cups
- measuring spoons

Objective: Explore what happens when dry and wet ingredients mix.

Science Inquiry Skills: measure, observe, communicate

- Write the recipe for play dough on a large sheet of paper. Display the ingredients and measuring utensils. Help children measure and pour the ingredients.

- At each step, encourage children to talk about how the mixture looks and feels and how it changes. If possible, take a photograph or draw a picture of each step.

- Glue photos to sturdy paper or draw each step on chart paper. Have children describe what happens at each step and record their words below each photo or picture.

Play Dough

Combine:

3 cups flour

$\frac{1}{4}$ cup oil

$1\frac{1}{2}$ cups salt

food coloring

Mix Ingredients.

Push the Car

Materials
- a toy car
- blocks
- cardboard
- connecting cubes

Objective: Explore which variables make a toy car go farther.

Science Inquiry Skills: predict, observe, communicate

- Explain to children that they will experiment to see how far the toy car will travel on its own. Have children build ramps from blocks and cardboard. Ask a child to send the toy car down the ramp without pushing it.

- Help children use connecting cubes to measure how far the car traveled from the end of the ramp.

- Ask: **How can we make the car go further?**
  (push the car, build a higher ramp)

- Ask a child to push the car down the ramp. Measure how far it went. Ask: **What happened?** Repeat, making a higher ramp and sending the car down the ramp with and without pushing the car.

Heat It Up!

Objective: Children will learn how hot water can change spaghetti.

Get Started

- **Prepare:** Cover the second and third pictures on Flipbook page 26.

- **Ask: Who has had spaghetti at home? Does anyone know how to make spaghetti? What do you need to make spaghetti?**

Read a Picture

- Show children Flipbook page 26. Ask children to talk about what they see in the first picture. **How do you think the spaghetti feels? Could you eat it? Why or why not?**

- Uncover the second picture and discuss what is happening. Ask: **What is the woman doing? Is the water in the pot hot or cold? How do you know?** (steam; it is on the stove) **How do you think the spaghetti will change? How do you know?**

- Uncover the third picture and discuss how it has changed. Ask: **How do you think it feels now? What caused the spaghetti to change?**

How did the spaghetti change

 ## Science Facts

The steam that rises from a pot of spaghetti is water evaporating, which means it is changing from a liquid to a gas. Water that has been changed into gas is at least 212° F. (100° C), the boiling point of water.

Reading in Science

- Write and say the word *did*. Ask children to listen for the beginning sound.

- Ask what other words they know that begin with the same sound. Record their responses, helping them see that each new word also begins with the letter *d*.

- Write *lid, kid, hid* below the word *did*. Ask, **What do you notice about these words?** (they all have three letters; they all end in the letters -*id*; they rhyme)

Informal Assessment

Check children's understanding of how food changes when heated by asking: **How do you think the spaghetti feels before it is cooked?** (hard, dry) **How does it feel after it is cooked?** (soft, wet) **Why does it feel different?**

26

Teacher Tip

If possible, bring a box of spaghetti to the meeting and give children a chance to touch it before they look at the first Flipbook picture. Then cook the spaghetti if you have a stove or hot plate available to use. Allow children to observe each step of the process.

More to Read

From Wax to Crayon, by Michael H. Forman (Children's Press, Inc. 1997)

This book illustrates how crayons are made.

Activity Ask children to discuss how crayons are made. Write their words on paper, and have children use crayons to illustrate each page. Make into a class book about how crayons are made.

Freeze It Up!

Objective: Children will learn what happens when a liquid freezes.

Get Started

- Ask children if they have ever had an ice pop. Ask them to describe the ice pop. (Possible responses: cold, sweet, purple)

- Ask: **Has anyone ever made ice pops? What did you do?**

Read a Picture

- Open the Flipbook to page 27. Read the question. Ask children to describe each step. **What do you think the girl did first? What did she do next?**

- Ask: **What is happening to the ice pop as the girl eats it?** (It is melting.) **Why is that happening? What other things melt?** (Possible answers: ice cream, ice cubes, icicles, snow)

- Ask: **What other liquids freeze?** Children may respond with things that actually will not freeze. Rather than just telling them it will not freeze, ask: **How can we find out for sure?** Plan with children an experiment to test their guesses.

How did the juice change?

 ## Science Facts

Juice is a liquid—a substance that flows easily and takes the shape of any container it is poured into. When a liquid freezes, it becomes a solid. Water freezes at 32 degrees Farenheit. When it changes back from solid to a liquid, it is melting.

Popsicle history: An 11-year-old named Frank Epperson invented popsicles by accident in 1905. He left a fruit drink out in cold weather overnight. It contained a stirrer, which froze right into it. Popsicles were originally called "Epsicles."

3

27

- Write the word *how* on the board.

- Ask children to think of words that rhyme with how. (now, cow, bow) List them on the board.

- Ask children what they notice about this list. (Possible answers: all end in *-ow*, all have three letters, they rhyme)

✓ Informal Assessment

Some children may not yet be able to use words like *liquid* and *heat* when they talk about how water changes from a liquid to a solid. For these children, model using these words as you talk with them about what they are doing at the water table, or when they are washing their hands, or helping cook snack.

Finger Play

I'd like an ice pop!

Here is a cup (pretend to give a cup)

Here is some juice (pretend to pour juice)

Here is a stick (pretend to place stick in)

Just put them together,

And put them in the freezer,

And wait for it to freeze (cross arms as if cold)

Into an ice pop. Please!

More to Read

Solids, Liquids, and Gasses, by Angela Royston (Heinemann, 2002)

Read this book to learn more about different states of matter.

Activity Fill a squeeze bottle with water, another with oil, and another with liquid soap. Have children squeeze a drop of each on a plate. Tilt the plate. **Do all the liquids move in the same way?**

Mix It Up!

Objective: Children will learn how matter can change when mixed together.

Get Started

- Ask: **What do you think happens when you mix sand and water? Dirt and water?**

- Ask: **What can you do with wet sand and mud? Can you do those same things with dry sand and dirt? Why or why not?**

Read a Picture

- Show children page 28 of the Flipbook and read the question.

- Point to and discuss the ingredients in the first row. Pass around a small cup with flour. Have children touch it and describe how it feels. Repeat with salt. **Does it feel like the flour? Why or why not?**

- **What happened when the ingredients were mixed together? How do you think the mixture would feel if you touched it?**

- Pointing to the pictures in the second row. Ask: **What colors of play dough do you see?** (yellow, blue, green) **How do you think the children made green play dough?** (They mixed two colors, yellow and blue, together.)

What is happening here?

 Science Facts

A mixture consists of two or more combined substances. Some mixtures are reversible. For example, if you mix salt into water and then let the water evaporate, you will be left again with salt. Other mixtures are not reversible. Once eggs have been cracked and mixed into a cake batter, there is no way to get them back. Certain mixtures are only reversible under extreme conditions. For example, when glass is recycled, it is crushed and mixed with sand (or other ingredients) at a very high heat. Then it is molded into new glass objects.

Reading in Science

- Ask children to listen for the beginning sound in the word *play*, and think of other words that have that same sound.

- Now write the words *play, day, lay, say, may,* and *tray* in a column. As you read each word, start by saying the first sound and the name of the letter. When you have read all the words, ask: **What do you notice about these words?**
(They all rhyme; they all end in *-ay; play* and *tray* both have 4 letters; the others have 3 letters.)

✓ Informal Assessment

Discuss with small groups of children how matter can change when mixed together. Have them give examples of ways the ingredients in the picture changed when mixed together.

28

EL

Provide children with an opportunity to explore mixing items together. For example, provide a dry ingredient, such as flour and a wet ingredient, such as water for children to work with. Model feeling the flour with your hand and saying *dry*. Invite children to feel the flour and repeat after you. Repeat with the water saying *wet*. Help children to mix the two ingredients together and describe how it feels.

More to Read

What's for Lunch? Milk, by Claire Llewellyn (Children's Press, 1998)

Read this book to learn more about how we get and use milk.

Activity Help children mix chocolate powder into milk. Ask: **How did the powder change when mixed with milk? Can we take the chocolate powder out of the milk? Why or why not?**

Push and Pull

Objective: Children will learn how objects can be moved by pushing and pulling.

Get Started

- Show a toy car to the class. Push it to a child. Ask: **What did I do to make the car move?** (push) Now pull the car back to you. Ask: **What did I do to make the car move?** (pull)

- Have each child push and pull the car to their neighbor. Have them say: *I am pushing (pulling) the car to (name of their neighbor).*

Read a Picture

- Open to Flipbook page 29. Have children take turns describing one thing they see happening on the page.

- Ask: **Where is the girl standing?** (in front of the pull-toy) **Where is the boy standing?** (behind the stroller)

- Ask: **When you push something do you move it away from you or towards you? When you pull something do you need to be behind it or in front of it?**

How can you make things move?

pull

Science Facts

In 1931 two men, Herman G. Fisher and Irving L. Price, created one of America's first popular pull toys that is still sold in toy stores today. At the time the toy cost parents under $3.00!

Baby strollers first came about in the early 1700's. The first stroller, or buggy as it was also called, was designed to be pulled by a goat, not the parent! The stroller changed over time with detailed designs that were sometimes too impractical. Strollers today are made to be safe and durable, and parents can even push them while they jog!

push

29

■ Reread the question: *How can you make things move?* Ask what they notice about the words *make* and *move.* (they both start with the same sound, they both start with the letter *m*)

■ Write the words *make* and *move* and have children help you count the number of letters in each word. Help children notice that they both have four letters.

■ Add an *s* to the end of each word, and ask children to listen to the ending sound of the words. Exaggerate the sound of the letter *s*. Ask children what sound they hear at the end of each word. **Is it the same in each word?**

✓ Informal Assessment

Observe children as you provide opportunities to push and pull objects. Have children tell if they are pushing or pulling an object.

Take a Trip

Take children around the school to look for things that move with a push and/or a pull. Each time they find something, record their discoveries by writing or taking a picture of what they found. Suggestions of things to look for: doors, cupboards, light switches, window shades, cafeteria trays, toy cars, carts.

More to Read

Pushing, by Patricia Whitehouse (Heinemann Library, 2003)

Use this book to help children recognize the many different things we push.

Activity   After reading, have each child draw something that they can push or pull. Write the word *push* or *pull* on the page and make into a class book.

Magnets

Objective: Children will learn what magnets do and where they can stick.

Get Started

- Before using Flipbook page 30 with children, cover the images with paper.

- Ask: **What is a magnet?** Show children a wooden block and a pair of scissors. Ask: **Will a magnet stick to these? Why or why not?** Try it. **What happened?**

Read a Picture

- Open to Flipbook page 30. Ask: **What do you think this boy is holding? How do you know?** Then read the question.

- Remove the first piece of paper. Have children discuss if they think the magnet will stick. Encourage multiple responses by asking: **Does anyone have a different idea?**

- After discussing the picture, have children try to stick magnetic letters to the same item. If you do not have the object pictured, supply a similar object.

Where will the magnets stick?

Science Facts

The first magnets were lodestones, chunks of a black, often metallic-looking mineral called magnetite (iron oxide). They were found in a place called Magnesia, in Turkey, which is why they were called magnets.

These days, magnets are human-made. Any substance that can attract or repel iron or steel is a magnet. It has a north and a south pole at either end, and its force is strongest at these poles. If you put two magnets together, their opposite poles (north and south) will attract, but their like poles (south and south, north and north) will repel each other.

30

Reading in Science

- Write the word *magnet* on the board. Ask children what sound and letter this word begins with. Encourage them to think of other words that begin the same way. Record their responses.

- Point to the letter magnet the boy is holding in the picture. Ask children to name the letter. Ask if there are any children in the class whose names begin with the letter *k*.

✓ Informal Assessment

Observe children as they figure out where magnets will stick. Provide children with magnets they can take home to further explore the properties of magnets.

Teacher Tip

Magnets will actually not stick to most surfaces! For this reason, children will need time to experiment with finding places where they will stick. To help children discover that magnets will not stick to all metals, have them experiment with coins. What coins will a magnet attract? What do they have in common? (color)

More to Read

Magnets, by Angela Royston (Heinemann Library, 2002)

This book explains what magnets are and how they are used in everyday life.

Activity Help children discover that objects are pulled by magnets. Give children strong magnets and a variety of items that are made of iron (nails, screws, cans, etc.). Ask: **Do magnets push or pull items?**

Observe and Assess

Use the Flipbook

Revisit the unit's Flipbook pages and discuss them with small groups of children. Have children demonstrate the difference between pushing an object and pulling one.

Use the Big Science Reader

Reread *Water* in the Big Science Reader, Vol. 2 with small groups. Before you read the words on each page, have children try to explain what the water is doing.

Performance Assessment

Have children discuss which objects magnets can stick to. Allow them to review their choices using magnets and small objects in the classroom.

Go Further

Pasta, Pasta

Materials
- spaghetti
- butter
- salt
- large bowl

Science Inquiry Skills: observe, communicate

Prepare: Have a camera ready to take pictures at each step.

1. Place a pot of water on a stove or hotplate.

2. While waiting for the water to boil, give each child a small piece of dry pasta. Ask: **What does it feel like?**

3. When the water boils, add pasta. Before it is completely cooked, take out some pasta. Let it cool and ask children to feel it. Ask: **How does it feel? Why does it still feel a little bit hard?**

4. When the spaghetti is cooked, serve a small portion to each child. Ask: **How did the spaghetti change?**

5. If possible, take pictures of each step. Glue photos or draw pictures of each step on sheets of construction paper and have children describe what happened. Write their words below each picture and make into a book.

School-to-Home

Be sure to send home the Home Letter from p. R12 with a list of books that your students can share with their families.

Physical Science   UNIT F • Matter and Motion

Dear Parents,

We are close to completing our unit about matter and motion. We have looked at what happens to water when it is frozen, melted, and mixed. We have explored pushing and pulling objects, and learned about magnets.

Here is a list of books that you can find at your local public library. You can read these books with your child to help reinforce what we are learning in class.

From Wax to Crayon
by Michael H. Forman
(Children's Press, Inc., 1997)

Solids, Liquids, and Gasses
by Angela Royston
(Heinemann, 2002)

What's for Lunch? Milk
by Claire Llewellyn
(Children's Press, Inc., 1998)

 www.macmillanmh.com for more science online.

Teacher's Notes

Start the Year

UNIT A • **Be a Scientist**

Dear Parents,

This year, we will be learning a lot about science, and helping your children learn how to think and act as scientists do. Scientists use what we call "inquiry skills" to do their work. They observe, compare, measure, classify (organize objects by like characteristics), communicate their questions and observations, put things in order (for example, from shortest to longest), make models, predict, investigate and draw conclusions.

When you take a walk in the park or go grocery shopping with your child, you can help them begin to use these inquiry skills. Ask questions such as, *What do you see? Which one is the biggest? How do you know that?* As you talk together, you will be helping your child learn how to think and act as scientists do.

Thanks for your support as we begin our work together this year.

Home Letters

Start the Year

Dear Parents,

We are finishing up our first unit in science. We have looked at how cats are alike, how butterflies are different, how to sort buttons into groups, how to look carefully at things through a magnifying lens, how to predict what might happen next, and many more activities.

Here is a list of books that you can find at your local public library. You can read these books with your child to help reinforce what we are learning in class.

Brown Bear, Brown Bear, What Do You See?
by Bill Martin, Jr.
(Henry Holt & Co., 1996)

Have You Seen My Duckling?
by Nancy Tafuri
(Morrow, 1991)

My Spring Robin
by Anne Rockwell
(Simon & Schuster, 1996)

Life Science

Dear Parents,

In this unit, we will be learning a lot about plants—exploring different types of plants, discussing what plants need to grow, and identifying the different parts of each plant, such as leaves, flowers, stems and roots. Children will have hands-on experiences sprouting seeds, growing small plants, and cooking with plants that people eat.

You may want to try planting and growing your own plant at home with your child. Using radish seeds or other fast-growing seeds, have your child help you plant them with soil in a small pot. Discuss what the plant will need to grow, and have your children help you decide where to place it so that it gets enough sunlight. Every couple of days, check the plant together to see whether it needs water and to see how it has grown and changed.

We look forward to sharing our learning about plants with you!

Life Science

UNIT B • Plants

Dear Parents,

We are finishing up our unit in science about plants. We have looked at what plants need to grow, various types of plants, the plants that people eat, and the different parts of plants. We have sprouted seeds, planted seedlings and looked closely at the parts of a plant.

Here is a list of books you can find at your local public library. You can read these books to your child to help reinforce what we are learning in class.

Growing Vegetable Soup
by Lois Ehlert
(Voyager Books, 1990)

Jack's Garden
by Henry Cole
(HarperTrophy, 1997)

The Tiny Seed
by Eric Carle
(Aladdin, 2001)

Life Science

UNIT C • Animals

Dear Parents,

For our next science unit the children will be learning about animals. We will talk about what animals need to survive—food, air, water and shelter—and about how they grow. The children will learn about different kinds of animals, including birds, insects and water animals.

Find opportunities to talk with your child about animals. If you have a pet, talk with your child about what your family *does* to take care of it. Ask questions such as, *What does your pet eat? Where does it sleep? How do you take care of your pet if it gets sick?* If you do not have a pet, you can visit a friend who does, or take your child to the petting zoo or a local farm.

We look forward to sharing our learning about animals with you!

Home Letters

Life Science

Dear Parents,

We are finishing up our unit in science about animals. We have looked at what animals need to survive and what happens as they grow. We have talked about different types of animals, such as insects, birds, and water animals, and have observed animals in their environment.

Here is a list of books that you can find at your local public library. You can read these books with your child to help reinforce what we are learning in class.

Polar Bear, Polar Bear, What Do You Hear?
by Bill Martin Jr./Eric Carle
(Henry Holt, 1991)

From Egg to Robin
by Susan Canizares
(Scholastic, 1998)

Are You a Grasshopper?
by Judy Allen and Tudor Humphries
(Kingfisher, 2002)

Earth Science

Dear Parents,

In this unit, we will be learning a lot about our Earth—describing different types of rocks and discussing different landforms and bodies of water. Children will have hands-on experiences exploring natural materials that are essential to our Earth, such as rocks, soil, sand, and water.

Here is an activity that you can do together.

You can explore rocks at home by helping your child start their own rock collection. Take short walks together in the neighborhood or in a local park, bringing along a container to hold the rocks. Encourage your child to find many different rocks and discuss how they are alike and different. When you return home, help your child sort the rocks in different ways. For example, by color, shape, size or texture.

We look forward to sharing our learning about our Earth with you!

Home Letters

Earth Science

Dear Parents,

We are finishing up our unit about our Earth. We have looked at various types of ground material, such as rocks, sand, soil, asphalt, cement, and grass. We have explored and sorted different kinds of rocks, and have learned about hills and mountains, oceans, lakes, and streams.

Here are some books that you can find at your local public library. You can read these books with your child to help reinforce what we are learning in class.

Rocks: Hard, Soft, Smooth and Rough
by Natalie Rosinsky
(Picture Window Books, 2002)

Let's Go Rock Collecting (Let's Read and Find Out Science, Stage 2)
by Roma Gans, Holly Keller
(HarperTrophy, 1997)

Dirt (Jump Into Science)
by Steve Tomecek, Nancy Woodman
(National Geographic Children's, 2002)

Earth Science

Dear Parents,

In this unit, we will be learning about day and night, seasons and weather. We will explore what we can learn about the weather from looking outside and what is different about each season.

With your child, find opportunities to look at the sky together. Ask your child questions such as, *Is the Sun out? How do the clouds look? What can you tell about the weather from looking at the clouds?* Then look at the sky at night. Discuss how the night and day sky look the same and how they are different.

We look forward to sharing what we learn about the sky and weather with you!

Home Letters

Earth Science

Dear Parents,

We are finishing up our unit about sky and weather. We have explored what is different about the sky during the day and at night. We have discussed what you can tell about the weather by looking outside and your child has learned about each season.

Here is a list of books that you can find at your local public library. You can read these books with your child to help reinforce what we are learning in class.

Night and Day
by Alvin Granowski
(Millbrook Press, Inc., 2001)

Wind
by Miranda Ashwell and Andy Owen
(Heinemann Library, 1999)

Watching the Weather
by Miranda Ashwell and Andy Owen
(Heinemann Library, 1999)

Physical Science
UNIT F • Matter and Motion

Dear Parents,

In this unit, we will be learning about how water changes when you heat it, freeze it, and mix it. We will explore the properties of magnets, and how pushing and pulling can move objects. Children will do some cooking in this unit—making ice pops to see how juice can freeze and melt, and making spaghetti to see what boiling water can do. They will also make play dough, to observe what happens when water mixes with other substances.

You may want to cook together at home. For example, give your child an opportunity to look at and feel rice before it is cooked. Then, let your child watch you make the rice. When it is cooked, eat it together. Talk about how the water changed the rice from hard to soft.

We look forward to sharing our learning about matter and motion with you!

Home Letters

Physical Science   UNIT F • Matter and Motion

Dear Parents,

We are close to completing our unit about matter and motion.
We have looked at what happens to water when it is frozen,
melted, and mixed. We have explored pushing and pulling objects,
and learned about magnets.

Here is a list of books that you can find at your local public
library. You can read these books with your child to help
reinforce what we are learning in class.

From Wax to Crayon
by Michael H. Forman
(Children's Press, Inc., 1997)

Solids, Liquids, and Gasses
by Angela Royston
(Heinemann, 2002)

What's for Lunch? Milk
by Claire Llewellyn
(Children's Press, Inc., 1998)

Bibliography

UNIT A Be a Scientist

A Dozen Ducklings Lost and Found
Ziefert, Harriet. HMC, 2003

Cat Count
Lewin, Betsy. Henry Holt, 2003

Do You Want To Be My Friend?
Carle, Eric. Putnam, 1988

Farm Alphabet Book
Miller, Jane. Scholastic, 1981

Guinea Pig ABC
Duke, Kate. Puffin/Penguin Putnam, 1986

EL **Lupe Lupita, ¿Where Are You?**
Lupe Lupita, ¿dónde estás?
Rosa-Mendoza, Gladys. me+mi publishing, 2002

My Five Senses
Miller, Margaret. Simon and Schuster, 1994

My Spring Robin
Rockwell, Anne. Simon & Schuster, 1996

The Button Box
Reid, Margarette S. Dutton, 1990

The Pumpkin Book
Gibbons, Gail. Holiday House, 1999

UNIT B Plants

A Handful of Sunshine: Growing a Sunflower
Eclare, Melanie. Ragged Bears, 2001

Carrot Seed
Krauss, Ruth. Harper/Collins, 1989

From Seed to Plant
Gibbons, Gail. Holiday House, 1993

EL **Fruits and Vegetables: Frutas y vegetales**
Rosa-Mendoza, Gladys. me+mi publishing, 2002

Growing Vegetable Soup
Ehlert, Lois. Voyager Books, 1990

Jack's Garden
Cole, Henry. HarperTrophy, 1997

One Child, One Seed: A South African Counting Book
Cave, Kathryn. Henry Holt, 2003

Planting a Rainbow
Ehlert, Lois. Voyager Books, 1992

Tell Me, Tree
Gibbons, Gail. Little Brown, 2002

The Tiny Seed
Carle, Eric. Aladdin, 2001

This Year's Garden
Rylant, Cynthia. Simon & Schuster Children's Books, 1986

Waiting for Wings
Ehlert, Lois. Harcourt, 2001

Wildflower ABC
Pomeroy, Diana. Harcourt, 2001

Bibliography

UNIT C Animals

A Hummingbird's Life
Himmelman, John. Children's Press, 2000

EL   Animals at the Farm, Animals de la granja
Rosa-Mendoza, Gladys. me+mi publishing, 2002

Are You a Grasshopper?
Allen, Judy and Humphries, Tudor. Kingfisher, 2002

Are You a Snail?
Allen, Judy and Humphries, Tudor. Kingfisher, 2000

Babies on the Go
Ashman, Linda. Harcourt, 2003

Baby's World: Baby Animals
DK Publishing, Inc., 2002

From Egg to Robin
Canizares, Susan. Scholastic, 1998

Guinea Pig ABC
Duke, Kate. Puffin/Penguin Putnam, 1986

Hello, Hello!
Schlein, Miriam. Simon & Schuster, 2002

Hermit Crabs
Schaefer, Lola M. Heinemann Library, 2002

In My World
Ehlert, Lois. Harcourt, 2002

Is Your Mama A Llama?
Guarino, Deborah. Scholastic, 1989

It's Time!
Deady, Kathleen W. HarperCollins, 2002

Make Way for Ducklings
McCloskey, Robert. Viking, 1976

A Place to Sleep
Meade, Holly. Cavendish, 2001

Polar Bear, Polar Bear, What Do You Hear?
Martin Jr., Bill. And Carle, Eric. Henry Holt, 1991

EL   ¡Salta, Ranita, Salta!
Kalan, Robert. William Morrow, & Co., 1991

Sea Horses
Schaefer, Lola M. Heinemann Library, 2002

Snails
Hughes, Monica. Raintree, 2004

The Animal ABC
Baker, Leslie. Henry Holt, 2003

The Journey of a Swallow
Scrace, Carolyn. Franklin Watts, 2000

The New Puppy
Civardi, Anne. Usborne, 2001

Turtle Splash! Countdown at the Pond
Falwell, Cathryn. Greenwillow, 2001

Wild Baby Animals
Wallace, Karen. Dorling Kindersley, 2000

Wild Birds
Ryder, Joanne. HarperCollins, 2003

UNIT D Our Earth

Beach Day
Roosa, Karen. Clarion, 2001

Dear Mr. Blueberry
Simon, James. Simon & Schuster, 1991

Dirt (Jump Into Science)
Tomecek, Steve and Woodman, Nancy.
National Geographic Children's, 2002

Everything is Different at Nonna's House
Cohen, Caron Lee. Clarion, 2003

Mud is Cake
Ryan, Pam Muñoz. Hyperion, 2002

Preschool to the Rescue
Sierra, Judy. Harcourt, 2001

Rocks and Minerals
Ricciuti, Edward R. Scholastic Reference, 2001.

Rocks: Hard, Soft, Smooth and Rough
Rosinsky, Natalie. Picture Window Books, 2002

The Little House
Lee Burton, Virginia. Houghton Mifflin, 1942.

The Seashore Book
Zolotow, Charlotte. HarperCollins, 1992.

We're Going on a Bear Hunt
Rosen, Michael. Simon & Schuster, 1989.

UNIT E Sky and Weather

A Bunny For All Seasons
Schulman, Janet. Knopf, 2003

Big Bear Ball
Ryder, Joanne. Harper Juvenile Books, 2002

Countdown to Spring! An Animal Counting Book
Schulman, Janet. Knopf, 2002

Days in Fall
Parker, Vic. Raintree, 2005

Days in Spring
Parker, Vic. Raintree, 2005

Days in Summer
Parker, Vic. Raintree, 2005

Days in Winter
Parker, Vic. Raintree, 2005

The Four Seasons
Black, Sonia. Scholastic. 2001

Here Comes the Year
Narahashi, Keiko and Spinelli, Eileen. Henry Holt, 2002

Leaves! Leaves! Leaves!
Wallce, Nancy Elizabeth. Cavendish, 2003

Like a Windy Day
Asch, Frank. Harcourt, 2002

Moon Glowing
Partridge, Elizabeth. Dutton, 2002

Night and Day
Granowski, Alvin. Millbrook Press, Inc., 2001

Rain Romp: Stomping Away a Grouchy Day
Kurtz, Jane. Greenwillow, 2002

Snow Day!
Lakin, Patricia. Dial, 2002

Splish, Splash, Spring
Carr, Jan. Holiday House, 2001

Tracks in the Snow
French, Jackie. Star Bright, 2003

Watching the Weather
Ashwell, Miranda and Owen, Andy. Heinemann Library, 1999

When the Moon is High
Schertle, Alice. HarperCollins, 2003

Wind
Ashwell, Miranda and Owen, Andy. Heinemann Library, 1999

Yellow Umbrella
Liu, Jae Soo. Kane/Miller, 2002

Bibliography

UNIT F Matter and Motion

B is for Bulldozer: A Construction ABC
Sobel, June. Harcourt, 2003

EL   Cars, Trucks and Planes, Carros, caminones y aviones
Rosa-Mendoza, Gladys. me+mi publishing, 2004

From Wax to Crayon
Forman, Michael H. Children's Press, Inc. 1997

Magnets
Royston, Angela. Heinemann, 2002

Pulling
Whitehouse, Patricia. Heinemann Library, 2003

Pushing
Whitehouse, Patricia. Heinemann Library, 2003

Solids, Liquids, and Gasses
Royston, Angela. Heinemann, 2002

What's for Lunch? Milk
Llewellyn, Claire. Children's Press, 1998

What's Up, What's Down?
Schaefer, Lola M. Greenwillow, 2002

The National Science Education Standards state that all teachers of science must have a strong, broad base of scientific knowledge extensive enough for them to understand the fundamental facts and concepts in major science disciplines. This glossary is designed to help the Pre-K teacher understand the basic facts and concepts of science.

A

adaptation Changes that take place over many generations in an animal or a plant that increases its chances of survival. A polar bear's thick, white coat is an example of an adaptation to the Arctic conditions.

air A mixture of nitrogen, oxygen, water vapor, and small amounts of other gases that is colorless and usually odorless.

altitude The measurement of height from sea level. Mount Everest is the highest mountain, with an altitude of about 29,028 feet.

aluminum A lightweight metal that is the most common metallic element found on Earth. It conducts electricity and is used to make overhead electric cables where light weight is important.

amphibian An animal that is cold-blooded and lives part of its life in water and part on land. Amphibians do not have hair, scales, or feathers, but they do have moist, smooth skin. They are often born in water and have gills. As they grow, they develop lungs and can live on land. They lay their eggs in water. Frogs, toads, and salamanders are amphibians.

animal A living thing that moves around, takes in other animals or plants as food, and is sensitive to its surroundings.

antennae Moveable, hair-like feelers found on an insect's head. They are also found on some shelled animals.

autumn The autumnal equinox, where day and night are equal in length, marks the beginning of the autumn season.

B

basalt A hard, dark-gray to black igneous rock formed by the cooling and hardening of lava from a volcano.

biologist A scientist who studies the habits and characteristics of living things.

birds Animals that have feathers, are warm-blooded, lay eggs, and have wings. Most, but not all birds, can fly. Birds have hollow, lightweight bones to help make it possible for them to fly.

bulb The stem of a small underground plant covered by leaves. Plant food is stored in the bulb. Tulips and daffodils are examples of plants that grow from bulbs.

C

camouflage A way some animals protect themselves by seeming to blend into their surroundings.

canyon A deep, narrow passage between hills. There is often a river at the bottom of a canyon.

carbon dioxide Formed when carbon combines with oxygen during burning or respiration, carbon dioxide is one of the gases in air.

characteristic A feature or trait of an animal or plant that is innate. For example, a characteristic of owls is that they have keen night vision.

cirrus The name given to clouds that are usually high, thin, and made of ice crystals.

classify To classsify is to put things into groups to show how they are alike.

clay A very small particle of soil that is smaller than sand or silt particles. Clay is used in ceramics and pottery and to make bricks and tiles.

clouds Clouds are formed by millions of tiny water droplets or ice crystals floating in air. Clouds are classified into three main types: cumulus (puffy) clouds are mountain or mushroom shaped; cirrus (wispy) clouds are high and feather; stratus (layered) clouds are low-lying clouds that make the sky look gray. Clouds along the ground are called fog.

coal Hard, black carbon that is burned as fuel. Coal was formed many millions of years ago from the remains of tropical and subtropical plants.

cold-blooded This term refers to the body temperature of reptiles, amphibians, and fish. Their body temperatures change when the surrounding water or air temperature changes.

communicate To share information with others.

compare To compare is to tell how things are alike and different.

conclusion To use information collected to explain a given phenomenon.

condensation The process by which a gas cools and changes into a liquid. The dew that appears on windows and mirrors is the result of the condensation of water vapor on cold objects.

continent The seven large land areas on Earth's surface (North America, South America, Europe, Asia, Africa, Australia, Antarctica) are called continents.

coral Coral are small sea animals found in many different shapes and colors. When they die, their limestone skeletons form coral rock. Coral reefs and tropical islands are made from coral rock.

cumulonimbus Clouds that are often called "thunderheads" that frequently bring rain, snow, hail, or thunderstorms.

D

decay The rotting and breakdown of dead materials caused by bacteria and other microorganisms.

desert A large area of land that has very little rain. Deserts can be hot or cold. Parts of the Arctic, for example, are cold deserts where water is trapped in the form of ice.

dew point The temperature of the air when it cannot hold any more water vapor. When air becomes colder than the dew point, water vapor forms clouds, fog, frost, or dew.

dormant An inactive plant or animal, for example, a seed in winter.

dune A mound or ridge of sand formed by the wind and found in deserts or along the sea.

E

earthquake Caused by the sudden shifting of rocks beneath the surface of Earth along a fault line.

Teacher Glossary

energy There are many forms of energy: electrical, chemical, mechanical, nuclear, light, and heat. Energy can not be created or destroyed, only changed from one form into another.

environment The conditions around a plant or animal that influence its life: temperature, light, living space, water, soil, and food source.

erosion The gradual wearing away of Earth's surface. It is caused by wind, waves, running water, rain, ice, or other natural forces.

evaporate When a liquid changes into a vapor or gas it evaporates. Heat increases the rate of evaporation.

F

family Biologists use this term for a group of living things with similar characteristics.

feelers The long, jointed growths on the head of insects and some other animals. They are used for touch and smell and are sometimes called antennae.

fin A moveable part of the body of a fish or other water animal. Fins are used for steering, swimming, and balancing in water.

fish A cold-blooded animal that has a backbone and lives in water. Most fish lay eggs in water, but some give birth to living young. There are about 30,000 different kinds of saltwater and freshwater fish.

fog A cloud near the ground.

force A push or pull that makes something move, or if already moving, changes its speed or direction.

fruit A fruit stores the seeds of a flowering plant.

fur The soft, thick hair that covers the skin of many mammals and provides insulation.

G

gas One of the three states of matter. Gas molecules move rapidly. Gases expand to fill up and take the shape of their container. When the temperature of a gas is lowered enough, it becomes a liquid. When lowered even more, it often becomes a solid.

gem A hard, usually transparent mineral that can be cut or polished. Gems come in many different colors and are often used for jewelry or decoration.

geologist A scientist who studies rocks and minerals, and the ways in which Earth has changed over the course of millions of years.

germinate Seeds need water, sunlight, and air to germinate or start to grow.

gills The part of the body of many water animals that enables them to get the oxygen they need in order to live.

glacier A huge sheet of ice that moves slowly over land. Glaciers form when, over many years, water freezes more than it melts.

granite An igneous rock that is hard and ranges in color from gray to pink or even red. It contains quartz, feldspar, and a small amount of other minerals.

graphite A soft, shiny, black mineral that is a form of carbon. Graphite, not lead, is used in pencils.

gravity The force that attracts things to move toward the center of Earth. The larger the object, the greater its gravitational force. Gravity is what causes people and objects to have weight on Earth and what makes objects fall towards Earth.

grub The worm-like form of an insect. A grub hatches and then develops into a pupa or chrysalis and then into an adult.

H

habitat The natural surroundings of a particular area where a plant or animal naturally lives and grows.

hail Frozen raindrops that grow larger as they are tossed around by strong winds in thunderclouds.

horizon The apparent line where the land or sea seems to meet the sky. Because Earth is curved, it is impossible to see beyond the horizon.

hull The outer covering of a seed or fruit.

hurricane Large, intense tropical storms that usually form in the late summer or early fall.

hypothesis A possible explanation for why something occurs. Until tested, a hypothesis cannot be proved nor disproved.

I

ice A colorless solid that is formed when water reaches 32 degrees Fahrenheit. Because ice is less dense than water, it floats on top of bodies of water.

igneous rock One of the three main kinds of rock. Igneous rocks are formed from the cooling and subsequent hardening of lava after a volcanic eruption. Granite and basalt are both igneous rocks.

inclined plane A simple machine that makes it easier to move a heavy load. It is set at an angle to the ground.

infer To use what is known to figure something out.

insects Small animals with three pairs of legs (6) and three segmented body parts: head, thorax, and abdomen. Most insects have one or two pairs of wings. Flies, bees, beetles, ants, grasshoppers, to name just a few, are all insects. Spiders, however, are not. They have eight, not six, legs.

instinct An animal behavior that is inherited, not learned.

investigate To make a plan to explore a question.

iron The most common metal on Earth. It is hard, gray, and very magnetic. When mixed with carbon and other elements, it becomes steel.

island A body of land smaller than a continent that is completely surrounded by water.

J

jade A gem, usually green, but also white, brown, or yellow. It is often carved and used in jewelry.

K

kernel The soft part of a plant seed that can grow into a plant. A kernel is protected by the husk.

lake A large body of water that is entirely or almost completely surrounded by land.

larva The early stage of insects that will change greatly in shape when they become adults. For example, a tadpole is the larva of a frog or toad.

lava Rock that is so hot that it has become liquid and flows through volcanoes and cracks in Earth.

legume A plant that creates pods that contain seeds. Peas, beans, lentils, and soybeans are examples of legumes.

life cycle A series of changes that living things pass through: born, grow older, reproduce, and die.

lightning When electricity in the atmosphere is discharged, a powerful flash can be seen. Lightning can appear between two clouds or between a cloud and the ground.

limestone A sedimentary rock made mostly of calcite.

liquid One of the three states of matter. A liquid has a definite volume, but not a definite shape. It can be poured, and it takes the shape of the container into which it is poured.

lodestone A magnetic rock, sometimes called magnetite, that was used as a primitive compass.

magnet An object with a powerful magnetic field that will attract iron, steel, nickel, and cobalt.

magnetic field The space around a magnet that can attract objects. The Sun, Earth, and other planets all have a magnetic field that extends for millions of miles.

mammals Warm-blooded animals with backbones that usually have hair or fur. They give birth to living young, and a female mammal produces milk to feed her young.

marble A hard metamorphic rock that can be polished. Marble can be white, streaked, or a variety of other colors.

mass The amount of matter in an object. An object's mass is not the same as its weight. Rather, it is a measure of its ability to resist changes in its motion. The greater an object's mass, the greater its ability to resist changes in its motion.

matter Matter can exist in three states; solid, liquid, gas. It is made of atoms, has mass, and occupies space.

measure To find out the length, width, height, temperature, capacity, or volume of something.

metamorphic A type of rock that has been changed by heat, pressure, or water.

meteorologist A scientist who studies weather patterns and forecasts the weather.

migration The movement of animals from one place to another. Migrations usually take place with the change of the seasons. For example, many North American birds migrate south before winter and return in the spring.

mineral An object found in the ground that does not come from living things and has a crystal form. For example, quartz and mica are both minerals.

model Something made to show how something does or might look.

Moon The Moon travels in an orbit around Earth. It takes 2912 days to completely circle Earth. Like Earth, it has a gravitational field. It is the pull of the Moon's gravitational force that helps create ocean tides.

mountain A very high outcropping of land. There are large, long mountains both above ground and along the ocean floor.

nimbostratus A dark gray layer of clouds that produce lengthy rain or snow showers.

nut A fruit with a shell that contains a seed or kernel. Nuts can be as large as a coconut or as small as a hazelnut.

nutrient Something that provides nourishment for a plant or an animal.

nymph A stage in the development of certain insects. A nymph looks much like a grown insect, but its wings are not yet fully developed.

O

observation The process of looking at something very carefully. Scientists take notes or make records of the things they observe.

ocean The large connected body of salt water that covers almost three fourths of Earth's surface.

oil A liquid substance that does not mix easily with water. Oil comes from three sources: from the ground (mineral oils) and from vegetables and animals (olive oil, animal fat).

order To place objects or events in a sequential arrangement.

organism Every living thing can be called an organism. Organisms reproduce, take in and use nutrients, and die.

peninsula A large piece of land that is surrounded by water on three sides. Florida is an example of a peninsula.

phase Astronomers refer to the apparent shape of the Moon by describing four phases: new moon, first quarter, full moon, and last quarter.

physical change A change in a substance that does not result in the creation of a new substance. For example, when water turns to ice, it changes form, but it is still the same chemical substance.

pistil A flower's female reproductive part that produces seeds.

plain A large span of nearly level land.

plant A many-celled living thing that usually makes its own food from carbon and water, using the energy from sunlight. Although scientists now know that some one-celled living things could be classified as plants or animals, they usually agree that the term plant should be reserved for multicelled organisms that can create their own food.

Teacher Glossary

pod The casing or sac that contains the seeds in some kinds of plants. Peas and beans have pods.

pollen The tiny, yellow grains produced by the male parts of flowering or cone-bearing plants. Each tiny grain contains one male reproductive cell. When there is a great deal of pollen floating in the air, it can cause allergic reactions in some people and animals.

prairie A flat, grassy plain with few trees.

precipitation The process by which water vapor condenses and becomes water or ice and falls to Earth as rain, hail, snow, sleet, dew, fog, or mist.

predict To predict is to use what you know to tell what might happen.

pressure A constant weight or force that acts on a surface. The air in our atmosphere creates pressure on Earth and is reported in units of force per unit of area. For example, air pressure at sea level is about 14.7 pounds per square inch. At the bottom of the ocean, the pressure of the water on the ocean floor is more than 8 tons per square inch.

prism Light is made up of different wavelengths. A glass prism is made in such a way that when light passes through it, the light rays are bent and the white light is split into the colors of the spectrum.

pupa A stage in the development of many insects. A butterfly is in the pupa stage while encased in its chrysalis.

Q

quartz A very hard mineral that, in its crystal form, has six sides and comes to a point. Quartz is often embedded in granite and sandstone. Agate, jasper, and amethyst are different forms of quartz.

queen A female in a colony of insects. There is usually only one queen in a colony. The queen lays eggs and produces young.

R

rain Precipitation that falls from clouds as drops of water. Rain is formed when water vapor in the air condenses.

rain forest A forest of tall trees where the rainfall is particularly heavy. Because of the lush foliage in these forests, very little sunlight penetrates to the forest floor.

ray A beam of light, heat, or other forms of radiant energy. A ray is also a group of large, flat, saltwater fish (stingray).

reproduction The process of producing offspring similar to the parents. Both plants and animals reproduce.

reptile A cold-blooded animal with a backbone that also has lungs. Reptiles have dry, scaly skin and lay eggs. Snakes, lizards, crocodiles, and turtles are all reptiles. Dinosaurs were prehistoric reptiles.

river A long body of water that flows in a channel and empties into a lake, pond, or ocean. Water for rivers comes from springs, melting glaciers, and lakes. On a steep hillside, the water can flow rapidly. Near the mouth of a river, it often flows much more slowly and is filled with mud and silt that has been washed down the river.

rock Most rocks are made up of two or more minerals. They can be very hard or very soft. Rocks are classified according to the way they were formed. There are three types: igneous, sedimentary, and metamorphic.

root The part of a plant that grows downward, absorbs water, holds the plant in place, and may also store food.

S

salt Salt is found in underground deposits and seawater that consists of sodium chloride. It flavors food, and because it kills bacteria, salt is also used to preserve foods.

sand Grains of rock, often quartz or feldspar, that are smaller than gravel and can be many different colors.

sandstone A rock that is formed when grains of sand bond together with minerals. Sandstone is a sedimentary rock and varies in color from yellow or red to gray or brown.

savanna A grassland of tropical Africa. There are some trees and shrubs that provide protection and shade for animals that graze on the savanna.

sedimentary Rocks formed by sediment, such as sand or mud, that is deposited and becomes compacted. Sandstone and limestone are examples of sedimentary rocks.

seed A part of a flowering plant that contains an embryo and the necessary food to enable the embryo to grow into a new plant.

shale A sedimentary rock made of compacted and hardened clay, silt, or mud. It forms in distinct layers and can be split easily. It varies in color from black or gray to brown or red.

slate A metamorphic rock that forms from shale. Slate also splits into thin layers. It ranges in color from gray to black or from red to green.

snakes Meat-eating reptiles that have long, narrow bodies, often just one lung, and a forked tongue. Some, but not all, snakes have venom glands and sharp fangs that can give a poisonous bite.

soil The top layer of Earth's surface. It is composed of rock and mineral particles and decaying organic matter (humus). Soil provides the nutrients that many plants need to grow.

solid One of the three basic forms of matter. The molecules in a solid have little or no ability to change places. Solids also have a fixed shape and volume.

sound Sound is produced when an object, such as a vocal cord or guitar string, vibrates. These vibrations travel in waves as they move through a substance.

spiders A group of small animals with a body divided into two parts (unlike insects which have three body parts). Spiders have a head and thorax, four pairs of jointed legs, usually eight eyes, and no antennae.

stamen The male part of a flower that produces the pollen the plant needs to reproduce. It is a slender stalk with an anther (pollen sac) at the end. The stamen is usually in between the petals of the flower on the plant.

star A large, glowing body in space composed of very hot gases, mainly hydrogen and helium. The Sun is our closest star. The stars in the night sky look like points of light because they are so far away from Earth.

steam When water boils, it produces steam. The steam is actually water vapor. When the water vapor molecules cool and join together to produce water droplets, the steam becomes visible.

stem The main stalk of a plant that bears leaves. The stem carries water and nutrients from the roots to the other parts of the plant and carries the food the leaves make back down.

stream A long, narrow body of water that runs along a channel or bed. Stream is used to describe bodies of water that are larger than a brook and smaller than a river.

Sun A ball of boiling hot gases with a temperature of millions of degrees at its core. Earth orbits around the Sun once a year. The Sun supplies Earth with heat and light.

T

tadpole The larval stage of a young frog or toad. Tadpoles live in water and have gills that enable them to get oxygen from the water. Gradually, tadpoles lose their long tails and gills, develop lungs and legs, and move from the water to the land.

talc A soft, smooth mineral used to make chalk, cosmetics, and other substances.

theory An explanation, based on observations and investigations, of how or why something happens. Theories can help us predict events or behavior.

thermometer A tool used for measuring temperature. Most thermometers are made of a thin glass tube containing a colored liquid. As the temperature rises, the liquid expands and the column of liquid rises in the thermometer. When the liquid cools, the column falls.

thorax In insects, the middle section of the body between the head and the abdomen. The legs and wings are attached to the thorax.

thunder The loud sound that follows a flash of lightning. Thunder is caused by the shock wave from the sudden heating of the atmosphere that happens when lightning strikes.

tide The regular rise and fall of the ocean. There is a high tide about every 12 hours, so there are usually two tides in a day. Tides are caused by the gravitational pulls of the Moon and the Sun.

tornado A small, violent, funnel-shaped storm. The swirling winds of a tornado can reach 320 miles per hour. Tornadoes can cause great damage as they roll across the countryside.

tree A large, woody plant with one main stem called a trunk. Trees also have leaves, branches, and stems, and are at least several feet above the ground. They are divided into two groups, those that keep their leaves all year (evergreen) and those that lose their leaves in the winter (deciduous).

trunk The main stem of a tree. The roots and branches are attached to the trunk.

tuber The underground part of a root or stem that contains stored food. Potatoes are tubers.

V

valley A long, narrow strip of land lying between hills or mountains. Because valleys are usually formed when land is eroded by rivers or glaciers, they often have fertile soil.

vapor A gas formed from something that is usually in a solid or liquid state. Water vapor is water in its gaseous state.

vertebrate An animal with a backbone. Mammals, birds, reptiles, amphibians, and fish are all vertebrates.

volcano An opening or vent in Earth's surface through which lava, hot gases, and ash flow. Volcanoes can be cone-shaped or an opening in Earth in which lava flows along the ground.

W

warm-blooded This term refers to an animal whose body temperature stays about the same regardless of the temperature of its surroundings. Birds and mammals are warm-blooded.

water A liquid that covers almost three fourths of Earth's surface. At normal atmospheric pressure, it freezes at 32 degrees Fahrenheit and boils at 212 degrees Fahrenheit. Without water, living things eventually die.

water cycle The movement of water from the atmosphere (water vapor) to Earth as it falls as rain or snow. This liquid ends up in bodies of water or the soil, where it slowly evaporates and returns to the atmosphere as water vapor.

wave A rapidly vibrating motion that passes through a medium, such as water or air, that does not change what it passes through. Light, heat, electricity, and sound all travel in waves.

wetland An area of land that often floods and where you can often see standing water for at least part of the year.

whale A large mammal that lives in the ocean. It is not a fish. It has lungs and must come up for air in order to breathe. Whales give birth to live young. They vary greatly in size. The blue whale is the largest animal that has ever lived.

wind A stream of air that moves over Earth's surface. It is caused by the unequal heating of Earth by the Sun and by Earth's orbit. When air comes into contact with the surface, it expands, becomes lighter, and rises. Cooler air rushes in to fill the lower space and this creates wind.

wool The soft, curly hair of sheep, goats, camels, and alpacas. This hair can be spun into thread and used to make cloth or yarn.

Y

year The time it takes for Earth to make one revolution around the Sun. It takes 365 days, 5 hours, 48 minutes, and 45.5 seconds, and that is why every four years we add one extra day to our calendar (leap year).

Z

zoologist A scientist who studies animal behavior, genetics, evolution, and ecology.

For additional glossary support, see:

Blackbirch Encyclopedia of Science and Invention, by Jenny Tesar and Bryan Bunch (Blackbirch Press, 2001)

International Encyclopedia of Science and Technology (Oxford University Press, 1999)

Science Dictionary, by Seymour Simon (HarperCollins, 1994)

Teacher Edition Credits

Photography Credits

All Photographs are by Macmillan/McGraw-Hill (MMH) except as noted below.

Tabb 1: Jeremy Woodhouse/Getty Images. Tabb 2: ©James Randklev/CORBIS. PK3: (t) Royalty-Free/CORBIS; (b) ©Brand X Pictures/PunchStock; (r) ©Imagebroker/Alamy. PK7: Ken Karp for MMH. PK9: Photodisc Collection/Getty Images. iii: Steve Bloom. v: (l,cr,br) Stockbyte; (tr) Burke/Triolo Productions/Brand X Pictures/Getty Images. vi: S. Alden/PhotoLink/Getty Images. vii: (l) Jack Milchanowski/Visuals Unlimited; (c) Pete Oxford/Nature Picture Library; (r) ©Arthur Morris/Visuals Unlimited. viii: (t) Don Farrall/Getty Images; (b) ©Roy Ooms/Masterfile. ix: ©Bob Krist/CORBIS. xi: PhotoLink/Getty Images. xii: (tr) Photodisc/Getty Images; (br) CORBIS; (cl) ©Brand X Pictures/PunchStock; (cr) Siede Preis/Getty Images. 1: (tl,tr) Photodisc/Getty Images; (bl,bcr,br) G.K & Vikki Hart/Getty Images; (bkgd) Keith Weller/USDA. 3: G.K. & Vikki Hart/Getty Images. 5: G.K. & Vikki Hart/Getty Images. 18: (cl) Burke/Triolo Productions/Brand X Pictures/Getty Images; (tr,br) ©Stockbyte. 19: (t) C Squared Studios/Getty Images; (b) Royalty Free/CORBIS. 21: (bkgd) Alan & Linda Detrick/Photo Researchers. 23: Jules Frasier/Getty Images. 25: Roger Phillips©Dorling Kindersley. 26: Ken Karp for MMH. 27: (bl) Photodisc/Getty Images; (bc) ©Christopher Campbell Photography/Stockfood America; (br) ©Eising Food Photography/Stockfood America. 28: (l) ©Brian Hagiwara/PictureArts/CORBIS; (t,r) C Squared Studios/Getty Images; (cl,cr) Royalty-Free/CORBIS. 29: (t) Royalty-Free/CORBIS; (b) Brand X Pictures/Punchstock. 29: ©Imagebroker/Alamy. 42: (r) Ariel Skelley/CORBIS. 45: ©Casey & Astrid Witte Mahaney/Lonely Planet Images. 49: (l) CORBIS; (r) Daryl Balfour/NHPA. 50: (inset l) G.K & Vikki Hart/Getty Images; (inset r) Photodisc/Getty Images. 53: (inset l) G.K & Vikki Hart/Getty Images; (inset r) Photodisc/Getty Images. 68: (l) Tom Brakefield/CORBIS; (r) ©Ulrike Schanz/naturepl.com. 71: Tom Stewart/CORBIS. 75: ©Richard Lord/The Image Works. 76: Ken Karp for MMH. 78: (l,tr) ©Brand X Pictures/Punchstock; (cl) ©Ken Wagner/Visuals Unlimited; (c) Colin Keates/Dorling Kindersley/Getty Images; (br) ©Mark Schneider/Visuals Unlimited/Getty Images. 88: (l) ©Marli Miller/Visuals Unlimited; (r) C Squared Studios/Getty Images. 91: Paul Barton/CORBIS. 93: (r) ©David Young-Wolff/Photo Edit. 95: ©Bob Krist/CORBIS. 96: (r) Ross Whitaker for MMH. 99: (t) Siede Preis/Getty Images; (b) Photodisc/Getty Images. 108: (l) ©Ariel Skelley/CORBIS; (r) ©Brand X Pictures/Punchstock. 115: ©Comstock/Punchstock. 118: (c) Siede Preis/Getty Images; (r) C Squared Studios/Getty Images. 130: (l) Dave King©Dorling Kindersly; (r) Brand X Pictures/Getty Images.

Illustration Credits

All illustration and childrens realia are by Peggy Klineman except as noted below.

Anthony Lewis: PK1, PK4, PK5, PK10, PK11, PK12, 7, 8, 20, 43, 51, 52, 53, 68, 79, 97, 99, 117, 131, R1, R3, R5, R7, R9, R11.

Song Poster Credits

Photography Credits

Song 2: Ken Cavanagh for MMH; Song 12: (tl) Brand X Pictures/PunchStock, (bl) Stockbyte/PictureQuest, (cr) C Squared Studios/Getty Images, (others) Ken Cavanagh for MMH.

Illustration Credits

Song.1: Pam Thompson; Song 3: James Williamson; Song 4: Judith Moffatt; Song 5: Ana Ochoa; Song 6: Michele Noiset; Song 7: Alan Flinn; Song 8: Bernard Adnet; Song 9: Jesse Reisch; Song 10: Melissa Iwai; Song 11: Terry Taylor.

Flipbook Credits

Photography Credits

Cover (l) C Squared Studios/Getty Images, (r) Renee Lynn/Photo Researchers; 1 Ken Cavanagh for MMH; 2 (farm)Deith Weller/USDA, (ducks)Photodisc/Getty Images, (cow, chickens)G.K. & Vikki Hart/Getty Images, (clouds)Jack Hollingsworth/Getty Images; 3 Ken Cavanagh for MMH; 4 (l to r) Photodisc/Getty Images, Dave King/DK Images, Ken Cavanagh for MMH, Jo Foord/DK Images, Alex & Laila/Getty Images; 5 Tom Stewart/CORBIS; 6 Ken Cavanagh for MMH; 7 (clockwise from tl) Isabelle Rozenbaum & Frederic Cirou/PhotoAlto, Eising FoodPhotography/Stockfood America, Isabelle Rozenbaum & Frederic Cirou/PhotoAlto, Ken Cavanagh for MMH (2), Schieren/Stockfood Munich/Stockfood America, Christopher Campbell Photography/Stockfood America, Photodisc/PunchStock; 8 (l) Wally Eberhart/Visuals Unlimited, (c) LUTRA/NHPA, (r) Royalty-free/CORBIS; 9 (clockwise from l) Bill Ross/CORBIS, Stockbyte/PunchStock, Guy Edwardes/NHPA, Gary Dyson/Alamy, Inga Spence/Visuals Unlimited, Alan & Linda Detrick/Photo Researchers; 10 (clockwise from tl) C Squared Studios/Getty Images, Jules Frazier/Getty Images, Royalty-free/CORBIS (4), Paul Poplis/Foodpix, Pete A. Eising/Stockfood Munich/Stockfood America; 11 Ken Cavanagh for MMH, (inset)G.K. & Vikki Hart/Getty Images; 12 (l to r) Jane Burton/DK Images (3), Dave King/DK Images; 13 (l)Julie Habel/CORBIS, (tr) Photolink/Photodisc, (br)Andy Rouse/NHPA; 14 (clockwise from tl)Mark Smith/Photo Researchers, James H. Robinson/Photo Researchers, Larry West/Photo Researchers, Stockbyte, Royalty-free/CORBIS, Larry West/Photo Researchers, Creatas/PunchStock, Joyce Gross; 15 (tl) Jose B. Ruiz/Nature Picture Library, (tc) Tom Brakefield/CORBIS, (tr)Arthur Morris/Visuals Unlimited, (bl)Steve Kaufman/CORBIS, (br) Stephen Dalton/NHPA; 16 (tl) Eastcott Momatiuk/Getty Images, (tc) Jeff Hunter/Getty Images, (tr) Casey & Astrid Witte Mahaney/Lonely Planet Images, (b) Jeff Rotman/Nature Picture Library; 17 (tl) Pete Oxford/Nature Picture Library, (tr) Klein/Peter Arnold, Inc., (bl) Jeff Vanuga/CORBIS, (br) Joel Sartore/Getty Images; 18 (tl) Ralf Schultheiss/CORBIS, (tr) Paul Barton/CORBIS, (bl) Tom Stewart/CORBIS, (br) George Shelley/CORBIS; 19 (clo kwise from tl) Siede Preis/Getty Images, Burke/Triolo Productions/Brand X Pictures/PunchStock, Wally Eberhart/Visuals Unlimited, Visuals Unlimited/Getty Images, Burke/Triolo Productions/Brand X Pictures/PunchStock, Dorling Kindersley/Getty Images, Marli Miller/Visuals Unlimited, Ken Wagner/Visuals Unlimited; 20 (t) Galen Rowell/CORBIS, (b) Rich Reid/National Geographic Image Collection; 21 (tl) Steve Terrill/CORBIS, (tr) Roy Ooms/Masterfile, (b) James Randklev/CORBIS; 22 (l to r) F. Damm/Zefa/CORBIS, Royalty-free/CORBIS, Richard Cummins/CORBIS, StockTrek/Getty Images; 23 Janine Wiedel/Alamy; 24 Paul Barton/CORBIS; 25 (l to r) Bob Krist/CORBIS, Ariel Skelley/CORBIS, David Young-Wolff/PhotoEdit, Tom Stewart/CORBIS; 26 (tl) Burke/Triolo Productions/FoodPix, (bl) Brauner/Stockfood Munich/Stockfood America, (c) LWA-Stephen Welstead/CORBIS, (r) Melanie Acevedo/FoodPix; 27 28 29 Ken Cavanagh for MMH; 30 (clockwise from tl) Ken Cavanagh for MMH, Royalty-free/CORBIS, C Squared Studios/Getty Images, Dave King/DK Images, Ryan McVay/Getty Images, Photodisc/Getty Images, Ken Cavanagh for MMH.

Big Science Reader

Photography Credits Volume 1

Cover (l)C Squared Studios/Getty Images, (r)Ariel Skelley/CORBIS; i C Squared Studios/Getty Images; iii Daryl Balfour/NHPA; iv Stockbyte; 1 (tr)Burke/Triolo Productions/Brand X Pictures/Getty Images, (others)Stockbyte; 2 3 G.K. & Vikki Hart/Getty Images; 4 AGE Fotostock/SuperStock; 5 (l)Jim Wehtje/Brand X Pictures/Alamy, (r)Stockbyte; 6 David Wrobel/Visuals Unlimited; 7 StockTrek/Getty Images; 8 Michael Pole/CORBIS; 10 (l)Roger Spooner/Getty Images, (r)Roger Phillips/DK Images, (background)Alain Altair; 11 (l, r)Roger Phillips/DK Images, (background)Alain Altair/Getty Images; 12 Phil Schermeister/Getty Images; 13 Patti McConville/Getty Images; 14 Lutra/NHPA; 15 Ann & Steve Toon/NHPA; 16 Ariel Skelley/CORBIS; 18 (l)Jurgen Freund/Nature Picture Library, (r)Daryl Balfour/NHPA; 19 (t)Bill Coster/NHPA, (c)Dave Watts/NHPA, (b)Anthony Bannister/NHPA; 20 (l)David Middleton/NHPA, (others)Mark Payne-Gill/Nature Picture Library; 20-21 John Shaw/NHPA; 21 (t)CORBIS, (c)Jany Sauvanet/NHPA, (b)Frank Greenaway/DK Images; 22 (tl)Karl Switak/NHPA, (tr)Gary Steer/Lonely Planet Images, (b)Ulrike Schanz/Nature Picture Library; 22-23 CORBIS; 23 (t)Jerry Young/DK Images, (cl)Ken Lucas/Visuals Unlimited, (c)Barry Mansell/Nature Picture Library, (cr)James Carmichael Jr., (bl)Jack Milchanowski/Visuals Unlimited, (br)Pete Oxford/Nature Picture Library; 24-25 (t)Steve Bloom, (b)Daryl Balfour/Getty Images; 26 (t)D. Hurst/Alamy, (b)Steve Bloom.

Photography Credits Volume 2

Cover (l)C Squared Studios/Getty Images, (r)Phoebe Dunn/Stock Connection/Alamy; i C Squared Studios/Getty Images; iii (hand)Siede Preis/Getty Images, (turquoise)Ken Lucas/Visuals Unlimited; iv Ken Cavanagh for MMH; 1 Don Farrall/Getty Images, (inset)Ken Cavanagh for MMH; 2 (t)Ariel Skelley/CORBIS, (b)Don Farrall/Getty Images; 3 Siede Preis/Getty Images, (inset)Ken Cavanagh for MMH; 4 (t)Myrleen Ferguson/PhotoEdit, (b)Siede Preis/Getty Images; 5 Photick/Alamy, (inset)Ken Cavanagh for MMH; 6 (t)Richard Lord/The Image Works, (b)Photick/Alamy; 7 8 StockTrek/Getty Images; 9 (clockwise from l)Wally Eberhart/Visuals Unlimited, Brand X Pictures/PunchStock, Siede Preis/Getty Images, Andrew J. Martinez/Photo Researchers, Ken Cavanagh for MMH, Brand X Pictures/PunchStock, Ken Lucas/Visuals Unlimited, (hand)Siede Preis/Getty Images; 10 Randy Faris/CORBIS; 11 AGE Fotostock/SuperStock; 12 Bill Losh/Getty Images; 13 Cindy Kassab/CORBIS; 14 Phoebe Dunn/Stock Connection/Alamy; 15 F. Damm/CORBIS; 16 Barbara Stitzer/PhotoEdit; 17 Gay Bumgarner/Alamy; 18 Roy Morsch/CORBIS; 20 CORBIS; 21 Alex L. Fradkin/Getty Images; 22 John Beatty/Getty Images; 23 Nancy Sheehan/PhotoEdit; 24 Robert Folz/Visuals Unlimited; 25 Atsushi Tsunoda/IMAGINA/Alamy; 26 Roy Ooms/Masterfile; 27 Jeremy Woodhouse/Getty Images.